JESUIT ART IN NORTH AMERICAN COLLECTIONS

JESUIT ART IN NORTH AMERICAN COLLECTIONS

By
Jane ten Brink Goldsmith
J. Patrice Marandel
J. Patrick Donnelly, S.J.
J. B. Harley

Published by
Patrick and Beatrice Haggerty Museum of Art
Marquette University, Milwaukee, Wisconsin

Exhibition 7 March – 16 June, 1991

Printed By
Morgan Press Incorporated
Dobbs Ferry, New York

Cover, Scipione Pulzone, *Pietà*,
Metropolitan Museum of Art, New York

PREFACE

St. Ignatius Loyola (1491-1556), whose vision led to the founding of the Society of Jesus in 1540, has contributed substantially to the cultures of West and East through educational leadership and the artistic patronage of his followers. Nowhere is Jesuit influence more evident than in the magnificent churches and arts of Europe and other lands where Jesuit missionary efforts were undertaken. It is fitting that these achievements be celebrated worldwide during the 500th year of St. Ignatius' birth, which coincides with the 450th anniversary of the Society. As a part of the official Inaugural Year Celebration, this exhibition honors Reverend Albert J. DiUlio S.J., president of Marquette University.

In conjunction with this worldwide celebration, the Patrick and Beatrice Haggerty Museum of Art is mounting the exhibition, "Jesuit Art in North American Collections." The exhibition includes a selection of paintings, drawings, prints, sculpture, liturgical objects, books, and maps. These are intended to give an overview of Jesuit influence on the visual arts. While most of the objects are European, the exhibition also includes paintings, maps, and other artifacts from the Far East.

Initially, the idea for the exhibition was proposed by Ross Fox, who served as curator from 1986 to 1987. We acknowledge with appreciation the use of preliminary research materials assembled by Mr. Fox. The curators responsible for organizing the exhibition are Dr. Jane ten Brink Goldsmith, at the Haggerty Museum of Art, and Dr. J. Patrice Marandel, at the Detroit Institute of Arts. Both have contributed essays and entries to this catalogue. J. Patrick Donnelly, S.J., professor of history at Marquette University, has contributed an essay on the Jesuit relationship to the fine arts from the sixteenth to the eighteenth century, and Dr. J. B. Harley, director of the Office for Map History, American Geographical Society Collection, University of Wisconsin- Milwaukee, has contributed an essay on Jesuit maps, which record Jesuit missionary activities and religious strategies.

This is the first exhibition on Jesuit art in North America. It offers a rare opportunity for both the general public and scholars to gain a better understanding of the Jesuit contribution to the visual arts. While much has been written on Jesuit iconography, Jesuit patronage, Jesuit artists, and Jesuit emblem literature, there exists no publication which brings all these aspects of Jesuit influence together. It is hoped that by bringing together paintings, prints, drawings, sculpture, emblem books, and maps, this exhibition will offer new insights on some of the more important contributions of the Jesuits to the cultures of both East and West.

Curtis L. Carter
Director

ACKNOWLEDGMENTS

Funding for the exhibition has been provided by the following sources: the Haggerty Foundation, the President's Inaugural Committee, the Marquette University Jesuit Associates, the Marquette University Religious Commitment Fund, the Ignatian Year Task Force of the Wisconsin Province of the Society of Jesus, and the Catholic Knights Insurance Society. For all of these contributions we express our sincere appreciation.

The cooperation of both public and private lenders has been essential to the success of the exhibition. Our thanks go to all who have made special efforts to accommodate the loan requests.

Special thanks are due as well to the staff of the Haggerty Museum, whose cooperation has contributed significantly to the success of the exhibition. In addition to the efforts of our curator, Jane Goldsmith, the following staff members are to be commended for their efforts: James Mazur, assisted by Tyler Bergstrom, designed and installed the exhibition; Marcia Eidel prepared funding proposals and coordinated publicity; Xiuqin Zhou served as registrar; Kit Basquin coordinated invitations and tours; Irene Juckem and Marilyn Meissner proofread the catalogue manuscript. Anne Kebisek and Anne Smith, student interns at the Haggerty Museum, provided invaluable assistance along the way.

C.L.C.

LENDERS TO THE EXHIBITION

The Allen Memorial Art Museum, Oberlin College

American Geographical Society, University of Wisconsin-Milwaukee

The Art Museum, Princeton University

The Dayton Art Institute

De Saisset Museum, Santa Clara University, Santa Clara, California

The Detroit Institute of Arts

The Lilly Library, Indiana University-Bloomington

The Mead Art Museum, Amherst College

Memorial Library, Department of Special Collections and University Archives,
Marquette University, Milwaukee

The Metropolitan Museum of Art, New York

The University of Michigan Museum of Art, Ann Arbor

Museo de Arte, Ponce, Puerto Rico

National Archives, Ottawa, Canada

The New York Public Library

Patrick & Beatrice Haggerty Museum of Art, Milwaukee

Philadelphia Museum of Art

St. Stanislaus Jesuit Historical Museum, Inc., Florissant, Missouri

The Sheldon Swope Art Gallery, Terre Haute, Indiana

The Snite Museum, University of Notre Dame

Valery Taylor Gallery, New York

Anonymous Private Collection

Table of Contents

International Standard Book Number 0-87462-904-M

Library of Congress and Number 91-60481

Distributed by The Haggerty Museum of Art

INTRODUCTION

Jane ten Brink Goldsmith

". . . . Wherein is inserted all possible inventions, to catch mens affections, and to ravish their understanding: as first, the gloriousness of their Altars, infinit number of images, priestly ornaments, and the divers actions they use in that service; that the most excellent and exquisite Musicke of the world, that surprizes our eares. So that whatsoever can be imagined, to express either Solemnitie, or Devotion, is by them used."

Grey Brydges, 5th Lord Chandos, *Discourse of Rome,* 1620

To an English traveller passing through Italy in the early part of the seventeenth century, Jesuit churches offered a veritable feast for the senses. A proliferation of brightly painted altarpieces, precious and ornate liturgical objects, and sumptuous decoration combined to produce a spiritual atmosphere saturated with physical exuberance.

From the 1580s through the mid-eighteenth century the Jesuits made a vital contribution to the visual arts. Catholicism had since the Middle Ages employed painting and sculpture as an effective means of inspiring faith; however, in the hands of the Jesuits the visual arts took on an altogether new and significant role. While functioning in accordance with Counter-Reformation imagery as an art of Catholic legitimacy, paintings and prints in particular, played a key role in allowing the early Christian past to be transformed into the living present for young Jesuit novices.

This exhibition is a tribute to the contribution that the Jesuits made to art tradition from the late-sixteenth through the mid-eighteenth century. It affords the opportunity to gather together some of the finest examples of Jesuit art in North American collections and provides an occasion to critically assess the peculiar relationship the Jesuits had to the visual arts, as well as their contribution to them.[1]

A few comments need to be made on the scope of the exhibition. Its primary orientation is European art from the late-sixteenth through the mid-eighteenth century. Italian art plays a dominant role in the exhibition as it did in Jesuit art during this period, however works produced in China, Japan, and India are also included. This reflects the way in which Jesuit art, like Jesuit science, crossed over the traditional boundaries of East and West, and offered a rare occasion for cultural interchange. Maps, which have a distinct place in visual history, are also included in the exhibition. The Jesuits played an important role in the mapping of Canada, the Great Lakes, and other parts of the New World; though in this exhibition we focus on maps of China as a means of underscoring the encounter of East and West under Jesuit auspices.

This exhibition sets out to define Jesuit art in two important ways. First, we define Jesuit art as art connected with Jesuit churches and colleges. From the sixteenth through the mid-eighteenth century, the Jesuits commissioned artists to provide paintings and sculpture for their churches. Andrea Pozzo's *Design for a Chapel in Vienna* [cat. no. 9] and his *Study for the Altar of S. Luigi Gonzaga in S. Ignazio, Rome* [cat. no. 19] are designs connected with Jesuit churches; his book on "Perspective," [cat. no. 38] included in the exhibition, is also related to the design and decoration of Jesuit churches. Secondly, we define Jesuit art as works which depict subject matter that is specifically Jesuit. While the Jesuits drew upon the conventional repertory of Catholic imagery, we can also identify a specific Jesuit iconography. Themes such as the glorification of the name of Jesus are strictly Jesuit, and the numerous works depicting Jesuit saints, such as Ignatius

Loyola, Francis Xavier, Louis Gonzaga, and Francis Borgia are also distinguished by their specifically Jesuit subject matter.

We are fortunate to have several contributors to the catalogue, whose differing areas of concern give a diverse sense of the issues at hand. The essays work together in a complementary fashion, often touching on the same material from different perspectives. Each essay, in turn, proposes a different sense of just how we define Jesuit art.

J. Patrick Donnelly's essay on the historical background places the Jesuit stance towards art in the context of the Counter-Reformation. His discussion of the *Spiritual Exercises* of St. Ignatius Loyola and the art theory of the Jesuit, Possevino, helps to provide a sense of what Jesuits expected art to do, and his consideration of the Jesuits as both patrons of the arts and as artists provides an essential dimension to an understanding of Jesuit art. His discussion of cultural interchange between European and non-European culture within the context of Jesuit missionary work, provides a perspective for the viewing of non-Western works presented in the exhibition.

My essay presents an overview of Jesuit iconography and discusses the evolution of Jesuit imagery from the late sixteenth to the mid-eighteenth century. *The Spiritual Exercises* of St. Ignatius Loyola, and other Jesuit writings, such as the *Evangelicae historiae imagines* (Antwerp, 1594) [cat. no. 36] and the *Imago primi saeculi Societatis Iesu* (Antwerp, 1640) [cat. no. 37], are discussed with the intention of evoking a sense of the special way of reading pictures that the Jesuits introduced.

J. Patrice Marandel's essay focuses on the decoration of the two most important Jesuit churches in Europe: the Gesù in Rome, and the Jesuit church, in Antwerp. His sensitive discussion of the differences between these two decorative programs provides a sense of two different Jesuit approaches to religious iconography. His discussion also makes us sensitive to the differences between Jesuits in the two leading cultural centers. Scipione Pulzone's *Pietà* [cat. no. 10], included in the exhibition, was executed for the Gesù, and the engravings by Jan Punt after Jacob de Wit are copies of paintings by Peter Paul Rubens which decorated the Jesuit church in Antwerp before their destruction in 1718.

The final essay by J. B. Harley is on the Jesuits and mapping. Discussing first the Jesuit contribution to mapping at large in the period under consideration, he then goes on to touch upon the Jesuits and the mapping of China. His notion of maps as a special category of visual imagery containing a Jesuit political agenda, suggests a similarity of purpose to paintings, drawings, and prints included in the exhibition, which often served at one level as propaganda and as a means of asserting Jesuit authority.

While the church had always been sensitive to the instructional value of the visual arts, for the Jesuits the instructional potential of pictures took on new purpose and force. The present exhibition, in a way that is characteristic of Jesuit art, is designed with educational purposes in mind. It is hoped that the presentation here of paintings, drawings, sculptures and prints with Jesuit maps and emblem books will encourage the viewer to look at these diverse kinds of cultural artifacts in relationship to one another. For to arrive at an understanding of what a map has to do with an illustration in an emblem book, and what both types of images have to tell us about religious works is to get at the very essence of Jesuit art.

NOTES

1. Important contributions to the study of the Jesuits and the visual arts serve as a foundation for the present exhibition. The first concerted study of the topic, R. Wittkower/I. Jaffe ed., *Baroque Art: The Jesuit Contribution* (New York: 1972), includes essays on architecture, painting, theatre and music connected with the Jesuit enterprise in Italy. Shorter studies, primarily on Jesuit art in Italy, have also been published. The most recent contribution to the topic is the exhibition, *Saint, Site, and Sacred Strategy* (Rome: Biblioteca Apostilica Vaticana, 1990). It addresses the Jesuit contribution to the urbanization of sixteenth-and seventeenth-century Rome, as well as issues pertaining to Jesuit church decoration and iconography.

Art and the Early Jesuits: The Historical Context

J. Patrick Donnelly, S.J.

I. The Reformation Crisis of Religious Art

During Loyola's lifetime the relationship between art and religion became the center of intense controversy. Christianity and the arts, especially painting, sculpture, and architecture, had been closely linked since Constantine the Great legalized Christianity in the Roman Empire in 313 A.D. From Constantine until the end of the Renaissance much of western art, indeed most of the best work, whether in painting, sculpture, or architecture, dealt with religious subjects or was linked to Christian worship.

The close links between art and religion did not go without challenge. Jewish tradition, ever mindful of biblical injunctions against idolatry, was far more cautious than Christianity in depicting God and biblical events in painting and sculpture. Islam was even more insistent that God not be pictured; even the Prophet Mohammed is normally pictured in manuscript illuminations with his face veiled, and the decorations in mosques are usually arabesques or graceful Koranic texts.

The Christian Byzantine Empire, which was in close contact with the Jewish and Moslem traditions, underwent an iconoclastic crisis in the eighth century when Emperor Leo III, supported by several bishops, attacked the traditional use of religious images; in 726 A.D. Leo ordered the removal and destruction of icons and crosses. His son Constantine V went further and developed a theology that rejected the use of religous images, especially the depiction of Christ. Iconoclasm enjoyed considerable support among Eastern bishops, but Constantine V aroused opposition, which was intensified by his execution of several monks. Defenders of the use of images triumphed politically and theologically by the early ninth century, and their victory is still celebrated in Eastern churches by the Feast of Orthodoxy on the first Sunday of Lent. In the West the iconoclasts found little support. The Gothic cathedrals are an oustanding offspring of the medieval marriage of art and religion.[1]

The Protestant Reformation brought on a sweeping re-examination of medieval theology and piety, including the use of images. Luther accepted the use of art to foster piety, but he attacked the Catholic use of arts to encourage the cult of saints. Several of Germany's best artists, such as Dürer and Cranach, embraced Luther's teaching and produced masterpieces of religous art. Far more radical than Luther on this point were other Protestant theologians, such as Ulrich Zwingli and John Calvin, who questioned the validity of religious images and reasserted the prohibitions against graven images of the Old Testament. Many historians of doctrine have traced their attacks on images on the theological/philosophical principle that the finite cannot convey or capture the infinite [*finitum non est capax infiniti*]. Because no finite image can properly mirror the infinite God, Zwingli and Calvin argued that attempts to depict God inevitably debase God and lead to idolatry. True to their convictions, they had religious art removed from the churches of Zurich and Geneva, but many of their followers were not as careful and engaged in iconoclastic riots that destroyed statues and paintings in Switzerland, France, England and the Low Countries.[2]

The official Catholic response to these Protestant challenges was formulated by the Council of Trent, which met on and off from 1545 to 1563. The Council's decree on religious art argued that the proper use of religious art was not idolatry since images were not to be honored for and in themselves, but only because of the holy events and people being depicted. Moreover, images were useful in lifting the hearts of the faithful to God since they made vivid for ordinary people the mysteries of redemption and moved Christians to love God and cultivate piety. But the Council also warned bishops to remove images that might lead the uneducated into error as well as to be on their guard against any art that might encourage superstition or lasciviousness.

Bogus miracle stories were to be avoided. The latitude that the Council gave to bishops meant that Catholic religious art and artists were henceforward to be under stricter church control.[3]

It is against the backdrop of the Zwinglian and Calvinist attack on religious art and its defense by the Council of Trent that early Jesuit interest in the visual arts must be viewed. The Society of Jesus was founded one year before Calvin took up permanent residence in Geneva and five years before the Council of Trent opened. The Council's decree has influenced Jesuit attitudes toward the religious role of art ever since.

The Jesuits rarely supported any specific style or school of art. Their patronage in art and architecture was eclectic and their influence diffuse; they were content with any artistic style that advanced their religious goals. The most fundamental of all Jesuit documents is the *Spiritual Exercises* of St. Ignatius Loyola, which teaches several methods of meditation. One method urges people making the *Exercises* to generate in their imagination various biblical events and scenes, right down to the concrete details of the place, actions and words of the biblical personages. This is what painters also attempted to do before depicting any biblical scene or the lives of the saints. Indeed, there is evidence that Loyola's directions in prayer were conditioned by his studying the illustrations in fifteenth-century Books of Hours.[4] Ignatian meditation was intended to sharpen the religious imagination and make people more sympathetic and discriminating when they viewed religious art. The methods of mental prayer taught in Loyola's *Exercises* were popularized in hundreds of meditation manuals written by Jesuits in the seventeenth century. Some of these attained an astonishing popularity; for instance the two stout volumes of Luis de la Puente's *Meditations on the Mysteries of Our Holy Faith* (first edition, Valladolid, 1605) enjoyed more than 700 editions in many languages.[5]

The Jesuits maintained close relations with several major Baroque artists. The Flemish artists Peter Paul Rubens, Anthony van Dyck, and David Teniers were all members of the Marian Sodality, which was perhaps the most important single way of spreading Jesuit spirituality to laymen. Peter Paul Rubens provided a series of ceiling paintings and two altarpieces for the Jesuit church in Antwerp, though most of these paintings were destroyed by fire in 1718. The altarpieces glorifying the miracles of Loyola and Xavier have, however, survived. Giovanni Paolo Oliva, General from 1664 to 1681, was the spiritual director of Gian Lorenzo Bernini, who designed the Jesuit novitiate church in Rome, the famous S. Andrea al Quirinale. Bernini also contributed illustrations to the eight volumes of Oliva's sermons. Unlike earlier Jesuit Generals, Oliva took an intense interest in architecture and encouraged ornateness and flamboyancy.[6]

The decrees of the Council of Trent on religious art were only general directives put together shortly before the Council ended. In the aftermath of the Council many Catholic churchmen wrote treatises defending the decrees and spelling out their implications.[7] An influential Jesuit example of these treatises was published by Antonio Possevino in 1593.[8] Possevino followed many Renaissance writers in basing his theory of art on the *Ars Poetica* of the Roman poet Horace, who had argued that poetry and painting had the same two-fold purpose: instruction and enjoyment. Both painter and poet, Possevino argued, must be men of learning if they are to recreate the world in all its complexity for their audience. After reviewing writers on painting, especially recent Catholic authors who insisted on art as the handmaiden of piety, Possevino launched an attack on art he considered lascivious.[9] There was a strong streak of puritanism in the Counter-Reformation that surfaced in Possevino's attack on the nude figures that were so popular in the mythological scenes done by mannerist painters of his day.[10] He held up as a model for artists his friend Bartolomeo Ammannati, who after years of sculpting sinuous mannerist nudes, underwent a religious conversion, repudiated his earlier work in a long and famous letter to the artists of Florence, and left his inheritance to the Jesuit college and church in Florence.[11]

Possevino, along with many others writing in the aftermath of Trent, insisted that artists strive for historical accuracy. Thus he objected to paintings that depicted St. Joseph as an old man, or St. Jerome wearing a cardinal's hat, or false miracle stories or incidents from the apocryphal gospels. All these elements had been commonplace in Renaissance art. Reacting against painters who used religious scenes largely to display their mastery of human anatomy, Possevino insisted that art should have a powerful psychological impact on viewers. "I firmly assert that the highest art, which imitates reality itself, both expresses martyrdom in the martyrs, tears in the weeping, sorrow in the suffering, glory and joy in the risen, and fixes them in our hearts. This is indeed the substance of art."[12] Jesuit insistence on dramatic impact and realism prepared audiences for the art of Caravaggio and Georges de la Tour.[13] Possevino and other Jesuits were particularly insistent that pictures of martyrdom should be bloody and vivid. Hundreds of Jesuits suffered martyrdom during the Society's first century, some in Europe, particularly England, but mostly in mission countries, especially Japan. Many Jesuit houses and churches contained paintings and engravings glorifying Jesuit sufferings.[14]

II. Jesuit Patronage of the Arts

Seventy years ago there was considerable discussion of what was termed the Jesuit or Baroque style in church architecture. Three considerations are related to this debate. The Jesuit mother church in Rome, the Gesù, which stands next to the building that housed the Jesuit Generals from Loyola until the early twentieth century, is widely considered the prototype of Baroque architecture. Certainly it is one of the most influential buildings in the whole history of architecture.[15] In addition, the Jesuits were expanding very rapidly during the late sixteenth and early seventeenth century and needed churches and colleges. These were naturally built in the emerging Baroque style. Finally, all plans for Jesuit buildings had to be submitted to the Jesuit General in Rome for approval. These three considerations suggest that the Jesuits were consciously and systematically spreading the Baroque style, especially in church architecture. Many features of the Gesù and later Baroque churches made them more suitable for preaching than Gothic or Renaissance churches; moreover, they provided a better stage for the Mass as a liturgical drama than did earlier churches. More dramatic liturgies could counter the Protestant emphasis on preaching and were consonant with the emotional role given to art by Jesuit writers such as Possevino.

Recently, art historians have abandoned the close identification of the Baroque style with the Jesuits. An examination of early Baroque churches in Rome shows that other new religious orders of the Counter-Reformation such as the Theatines and Oratorians were also building in the Baroque style. Furthermore, the modifications made by the Jesuit General and his advisors to plans submitted to them indicate that their overriding interest was in practical questions of cost, site, and acoustics rather than in artistic style. Many Jesuit buildings were designed in a "Baroque" style, but that was simply the dominant style of the period rather than a taste specific to the Jesuits. Indeed, Jesuit churches tended to be plain rather than flamboyant, unless wealthy patrons were contributing to the costs. When the Jesuits themselves paid for paintings and frescos, the salary rather than the skill and style of the artist was a major concern.

The best art in Jesuit churches was usually commissioned by non-Jesuit patrons, either churchmen or lay people. It was the patrons, who paid the bills, that set the specifications for artists. The interaction of Jesuits and their patrons is neatly illustrated by the story of the Gesù itself. The main patron of the church was the wealthy cardinal Alessandro Farnese, who assigned the principal architects Giacomo da Vignola and Giacomo della Porta. When the Jesuits asked the Cardinal for a flat roof to insure better acoustics, the Cardinal ignored them and wrote a famous letter to Vignola insisting on a vaulted roof.[16] After providing decorations for the high altar, Farnese initiated a project for decorating the dome; his death in 1589 halted the work. The famous ceiling fresco of the Church, Gaulli's *Triumph of the Name of Jesus*, was not completed until ninety years later. Meanwhile, decoration of the side chapels went forward. The painters for the altars were chosen by the various donors, but the painters of the chapel vaults were chosen by the Jesuits, usually second-rate artists who could be hired cheaply. The resulting frescos have a considerable thematic unity, since the Jesuits were able to control this, but Howard Hibbard finds these chapels a stylistic babel so that a "conscientious pictorial trip through the Gesù of 1600 would have given an aesthete artistic indigestion caused by the jumble of style."[17]

III. Jesuit Artists

The early Society of Jesus produced few artists compared to the number of illustrious Jesuit theologians, philosophers, and writers. None of the artists were first-rate. There are social causes for this relative paucity. Most Jesuits came from Jesuit colleges and upper class families and entered the order before their twentieth birthday. Thereafter they were subjected to a rigorous academic training that emphasized literature, philosophy and theology. The visual arts played little role in this training. Moreover, painting and sculpture were still widely considered skilled crafts unsuited for gentlemen or clergymen. Most Jesuit artists were not priests, but lay brothers, who had acquired their artistic training before entering the novitiate. Some of these brothers possessed considerable skill, and Jesuit superiors had the wisdom to refrain from assigning them to the community kitchen, carpenter shop, or porter's desk where most brothers, largely illiterate, were employed. The most famous of these brothers was Andrea Pozzo (1642-1709), who painted the triumphal ceiling fresco in S. Ignazio in Rome and wrote an important book on perspective included in this exhibition. Brother Giovanni Tristano designed a wide range of Jesuit churches and buildings throughout Italy from 1563 till his death in 1575; he served as an assistant to Vignola in designing the Gesù. Many brothers who showed artistic gifts were sent to mission countries, here persons skilled in Western art could not be hired.[18]

The Jesuit colleges of the Renaissance were famous for their drama; roughly 1,000 dramatic pieces survive out of a staggering total estimated at 100,000. These plays often involved elaborate stage scenery, much of it including painted architecture in *trompe l'oeil* perspective.[19]

Perhaps in no area was collaboration between Jesuits and lay artist so close than in the production of emblem books. The pioneer emblem book, published by the Italian humanist Andrea Alciati in 1522, began a flood that did not abate until 1700. It is difficult to define and describe emblem books because no books or art forms quite match them today. Emblems combine elements of poetry, comic books and crossword puzzles. The standard emblem usually occupied a full page, but sometimes more; at the top would be an engraving, then a motto or aphorism, and then a poem. In isolation the meaning of the three elements was usually deliberately enigmatic; together they were designed to clarify and re-enforce one another, often requiring a good deal of learning and reflection to discover the meaning of the whole. The joy of discovery might be compared to the sense of accomplishment at completing a crossword puzzle, but on a higher artistic-literary level. Good emblems clearly required very close collaboration between the artist/engraver who made the picture and the writer who supplied the motto and wrote the poem. In early modern Europe thousands of emblem books appeared in Latin and all major vernacular languages of Europe. The Jesuits published more than four hundred emblem books, plus many other works that contained emblems. The most prolific single Jesuit emblem writer was Claude-François Menestrier of Lyon, who published sixteen emblem books; he also published a work on dance in 1682 that has been called "the first comprehensive history and theory of the dance ever written."[20] Jesuit emblems deal with a wide range of topics but stressed Catholic religious themes; since these books were designed for a sophisticated readership, many were more philosophical than overtly pious. The current exhibition at the Haggerty Museum of Art includes a massive work published by the Belgian Jesuits, *Imago primi saeculi Societatis Iesu*, (Antwerp: Plantin, 1640), to commemorate the hundredth anniversary of the Society of Jesus. It contains 132 emblems illustrating Jesuit activity and history.[21]

IV. The Jesuits and Stylistic Interchange around the World

Central to the tasks that Loyola assigned the Jesuits were foreign missions, a project pioneered by St. Francis Xavier. In their efforts to convert the peoples of Africa, Asia and the Americas, they employed art no less than in Europe. Western art brought by Jesuit missionaries to foreign places employed techniques that Africans, Asians, and native Americans could appreciate and adapt to their own work.

The most striking evidence of this comes from Japan. It was St. Francis Xavier himself who first brought Western paintings to Japan and was struck by Japanese interest in them. Two schools set up by the Jesuits in 1580 taught Western painting to their students, but the main impact came with the arrival of the Jesuit brother Giovanni Niccolo in 1583. He continued to paint in churches and to teach painting in Nagasaki till 1614, when Jesuit missionaries were expelled. One of the many Japanese he trained in Western art was Blessed Leonard Kimura, the Jesuit martyr. The Jesuit schools also taught printing and copper engraving. The names of six other Jesuit brothers trained by Niccolo are known and some works survive. The style that evolved from these Western contacts is Namban art: the arrangements of figures and subject matter borrow much from the West, but the color has a distinctly Japanese intensity. Many Namban paintings are on folding screens, frequently with six vertical panels. The paintings done by Japanese Jesuit painters have religious themes but those done by laymen are usually on secular subjects. Because of the persecution of Christians in Japan, much of this art was kept hidden for centuries. A painting of the fifteen mysteries of the rosary together with Loyola and Xavier in prayer was discovered only in 1920. Some of this art was brought to Europe in the seventeenth century, for instance two pictures of martyrdoms in Japan kept in the Gesù.[22]

A century after Namban art in Japan, many Chinese artists were influenced by the Jesuit brother Giuseppe Castiglione (1688-1766), who had been trained in Italy by Brother Andrea Pozzo, the most accomplished of Jesuit painters. He was presented to the Chinese Emperor K'ang Hsi in 1715 and spent the next several years at Beijing mastering the Chinese art of painting in ink on silk. For Emperor Yung Cheng (1723-1735) he painted his master work, *One Hundred Horses*. This work is a synthesis of Western and Chinese styles, which delighted the Emperor. The next Emperor Ch'ien Lung (1736-1795) was deeply interested in art and visited Castiglione's studio almost daily and made the Jesuit a mandarin of the third rank. He also built a series of Baroque palaces based on designs provided by Castiglione.[23] A monograph and several postage stamps reproducing his paintings issued in Taiwan have highlighted his contribution to the dialogue of Eastern and Western art.[24]

The interchange was not totally one-sided. The French Jesuits at Beijing sent back Chinese books and art to Louis XIV that help stir Western interest in China and Chinese art. During the early eighteenth century, first in France and then in upper-class circles through much of Europe, there was a rage for wall decorations, furniture and porcelain in a style called Chinoiserie, which attempted, often not very successfully, to imitate Chinese art.[25]

The Western impact was even greater in Latin America, where Jesuit artists played a crucial role in transmitting Western art to other cultures. In Brazil alone twenty-one Jesuit architects were at work. Here the Milanese Gianbattista Primoli (1673-1747), who had worked as an architect and professor of architecture before becoming a Jesuit brother, deserves mention; after designing several churches in Buenos Aires he was assigned to the missions among the Guarani Indians of Paraguay, where he collaborated with native craftsmen on several projects. These Jesuits missions, or reductions, in Paraguay were highlighted recently by the movie, *The Mission*. The buildings that the Jesuits and their Indian converts built were richly decorated with sculpture that combined Baroque and Amerindian styles to achieve an art whose primitive quality is at once delightful and devout. Decorative motifs based on tropical flora and fauna add an exotic touch for those accustomed to European Baroque motifs. The Paraguayan government has sponsored the preservation and restoration of many churches, where decay and neglect have not proceeded too far.[26]

In summary, the Jesuit contribution to the visual arts in the sixteenth and seventeenth centuries took many forms. Loyola and Jesuit writers sharpened the religious imagination and thereby encouraged a taste for the vivid depiction of biblical and religious events. Jesuit writers such as Possevino defended the use of religious art against attack. The Jesuits commissioned the building of hundreds of churches, mainly in the Baroque style, secured patrons for their construction, and filled their interiors with paintings and sculpture. Some Jesuits, mainly lay brothers, were themselves notable artists. Finally the Jesuits played a central role in spreading European artistic style and Jesuit iconography to Asia, Africa and the Americas.

NOTES

1. The most recent discussion of Iconoclastic Crisis in Eastern Orthodoxy is by the distinguished historian of theology, Jaroslav Pelikan, *Imago Dei: The Byzantine Apology for Icons*, (Princeton: Priceton University Press, 1990).

2. Carl G. Christensen, *Art and the Reformation in Germany*, (Detroit/Athens, Ohio: Wayne State University Press/Ohio University Press, 1979); Carlos M. N. Eire, *War Against the Idols: The Reformation of Worship from Erasmus to Calvin*, (Cambridge: Cambridge University Press, 1986); Charles Garside, *Zwingli and the Arts*, (New Haven: Yale University Press, 1966).

3. A translation of Trent's decree on sacred images is printed in H. J. Schroeder, *Canons and Decrees of the Council of Trent*, (St. Louis: Herder, 1941) 215-217.

4. C.J. McNaspy, "Art in Jesuit Life," *Studies in the Spirituality of Jesuits*, Vol. 3, (1973), 103.

5. The best overview of Jesuit spiritual writers remains Joseph de Guibert, *The Jesuits: Their Spiritual Doctrine and Practice*, translated by William J. Young, (Chicago: Loyola University Press, 1964). Émile Mâle traces in some detail how the *Spiritual Exercises* and Jesuit retreat masters and writers influenced the depiction of death in the late sixteenth and early seventeenth century: *L'art religieux après le Concile de Trente. Étude sur l'iconographie de la fin du XVIe siècle, du XVIIe siècle et du XVIIIe siècle*, (Paris: A. Colin, 1951) 206-214.

6. McNaspy, "Art in Jesuit Life," 96; on Oliva and Bernini, see Francis Haskell, "The Role of Patrons: Baroque Style Changes," in Rudolf Wittkower and Irma B. Jaffe, editors, *Baroque Art: The Jesuit Contribution*, (New York: Fordham University Press, 1972) 57-60; on Ruben's work in the Jesuit church in Antwerp, Rudolf Wittkower, "Problems of the Theme," in Wittkower and Jaffe, 10; the role of the Jesuit sodalities is central to Louis Chatellier's study, *The Europe of the Devout: the Catholic Reformation and the Formation of a New Society*, (Cambridge: Cambridge University Press, 1989).

7. The two most influential bishops in Northern Italy in the decades after Trent were Cardinal Saint Carlo Borromeo in Milan and Cardinal Gabriele Paleotti in Bologna. Both wrote treatises on religious art that have been recently reprinted, along with many other such treatises, in Paola Barocchi, *Trattati d'arte del Cinquecento, fra manierismo e controriforma*, (Bari: Laterza, 1960-1962); for Borromeo, III, 1-113, for Paleotti, II, 117-509. A good review of the literature on the Counter-Reformation and art is Paolo Prodi, "Ricerche sulla teorica delle arte figurative nella riforma cattolica" in *Archivio italiano per la storia della pietà*, 4, 1965, 121-212, especially pages 123-140. A good study of how this religious atmosphere affected the greatest artist of the age is Romeo de Maio's *Michelangelo e la controriforma*, (Bari: Laterza, 1978).

8. The treatise first appeared in Possevino's massive *Biblioteca Selecta*, issued by the Vatican Press in 1593. It was reprinted in revised editions of the *Bibliotheca Selecta*, (Venice: Salacatius, 1603) and (Cologne: Gymnicus, 1607). The treatise on poetry and art was printed separately at Lyons in 1594 and 1595. References here are to the 1603 Venetian edition. Possevino's treatise is discussed by Pierre Janelle, *The Catholic Reformation*, (Milwaukee: Bruce, 1963), 161-166, and by Anthony Blunt, *Artistic Theory in Italy, 1450-1600*, (Oxford: Oxford University Press, 1962), 112, 114, 118, 127. The most detailed study of Possevino as art critic is John Patrick Donnelly, S.J., "Antonio Possevino, S.J., as a Counter-Reformation Critic of the Arts," in *Journal of the Rocky Mountain Medieval and Renaissance Association* 3 (1982) 153-164. The treatment of Possevino here draws on that study.

9. Possevino, II, 539-542.

10. Possevino, II, 547-549.

11. Donnelly, 156-159. Ammannati's letter is reprinted in Barocchi, III, 115-123.

12. Possevino, II, 545.

13. On the impact of the decrees of Trent and the Catholic use of art as a weapon against Protestantism, see Mâle, 1-107.

14. Mâle, 109-121.

15. For a discussion of the Gesù, see James S. Ackerman, "The Gesù in the Light of Contemporary Church Design," in Wittkower and Jaffe, 15-28.

16. Francis Haskell, "The Role of Patrons: Baroque Style Changes," in Wittkower and Jaffe, 51-62, especially 52.

17. Howard Hibbard, "*Ut pictura sermones*: The First Painted Decorations of the Gesù," in Wittkower and Jaffe, 40.

18. For Pozzo see N. Carbonieri, *Andrea Pozzo*, (Trent, 1961); for Valeriano, see Pietro Pirri, *Giuseppe Valeriano, S.I.: Architetto e Pittore, 1542-1596* (Rome, 1970); for Tristano, see Pietro Pirri, *Giovanni Tristano e i primordi della architettura Gesuitica*, (Rome, 1955); McNaspy, "Art in Jesuit Life," 95, notes that thirty-four Jesuit architects worked in France.

19. McNaspy, "Art in Jesuit Life," 97.

20. McNaspy, "Art in Jesuit Life," 97.

21. A good introduction to emblems is Peter Daly, *Literature in the Light of the Emblem*, (Toronto: Toronto University Press, 1979). A monumental survey is Arthur Henkel and Albrecht Schone, *Emblemata, Handbuch zur Sinnbildkunst des XVI. und XVII. Jahrhunderts*, (Stuttgart: J.B. Metzler, 1967). Jesuit emblem books have been surveyed by Richard Dimler in a series of articles in English in *Archivum Historicum Societatis Iesu:* for German and Austrian Jesuits, 45 (1976) 129-138; for Belgian Jesuits, 46 (1977) 377-387; for French Jesuits, 47 (1978) 241-250; for emblem books issued not by authors but by Jesuit colleges, 48 (1979) 277-309. The Spanish and Italian Jesuits were also prolific in publishing emblem books.

22. See Fernando G. Gutiérrez, "A Survey of Namban Art," in Michael Cooper, editor, *The Southern Barbarians: the First Europeans in Japan*, (Tokyo and Palo Alto: Kodansha International in cooperation with Sophia University, [1971], 147-206; this essay is rich in reproductions of Namban art, many in color. For the rosary with Loyola and Xavier, 155.

23. Mary Lawton, "Castiglione: Artist Missionary," *Company*, Spring, 1988, 18-21; McNaspy, "Art in Jesuit Life," 96; Oliver Impey, *Chinoiserie: The Impact of Oriental Styles on Western Art and Decoration*, (New York, Scribners, 1977) 49.

24. McNaspy, "Art in Jesuit Life," 96; the monograph is Cécile and Michel Beurderley, *Giuseppe Castiglione: A Jesuit Painter at the Court of the Chinese Emperors*, (Rutland: Temple, 1972).

25. Impey, 78 and passim.

26. C. J. McNaspy, *Lost Cities of Paraguay: Art and Architecture of the Jesuit Reductions, 1607-1767* (Chicago: Loyola University Press, 1982) is lavishly illustrated with these works; for Primoli, 73-81. Also useful is Mario J. Buschizzo, "La Arquitectura en madera de las misiones del Paraguay, Chiquitos, Mojos y Maynas," in Millard Meiss et al., *Latin American Art and the Baroque Period in Europe: Studies in Western Art*, [Acts of the Twentieth International Congress of the History of Art] (Princeton: Princeton University Press, 1963) III, 173-190.

Jesuit Iconography: The Evolution of a Visual Idiom

Jane ten Brink Goldsmith

I. The Formation of a Jesuit Iconography

By the 1580s in Italy there had emerged what one may specifically refer to as a Jesuit iconography.[1] The theme of martyrdom, not in itself new to Christian imagery, was taken up by the Jesuits in their early stage of church decoration as the most suitable subject for altarpieces and other sorts of paintings.[2] To consider the depiction of martyrdom as the first stage in the evolution of Jesuit imagery is to address the very special way in which the Jesuits made use of the visual arts.

Three of the earliest Jesuit establishments in Rome to be decorated with paintings contain picture cycles dealing with Christian martyrs. In the 1570s, the private quarters of S. Andrea al Quirinale were decorated with scenes of the martyrdoms of recent Jesuit missionaries.[3] This was followed in 1582 by a series of paintings depicting English martyrdoms from early times until "the present" for the English College, St. Thomas of Canterbury.[4] In 1582 S. Stefano Rotondo, the Hungarian College, received a picture cycle consisting of thirty scenes of martyrdom from early Christian times.[5]

During the 1580s, when martyrdom emerged as a preferred theme in the decoration of Jesuit establishments, Roberto Bellarmino, a Jesuit, and Cesare Baronio, an Oratorian, were at work on a revision of the *Roman Martyrology*, a project initiated by Pope Gregory XIII.[6] While the topic of early Christian martyrs was of fundamental concern to the Counter-Reformation church, it had special relevance for the Society of Jesus.

The Jesuits and the Oratorians were leading orders of the Counter-Reformation.[7] Both sought to combat heresy with equal zeal, yet a fundamental difference separates the two. Whereas missionary work came to be a basic aspect of the Jesuit enterprise, this type of activity did not constitute part of the Oratorian religious agenda. Hence, the brutal wave of persecutions that the Jesuit missionaries experienced in distant lands gave special relevance to paintings depicting martyrdom.

Both missionary work and the Jesuit preoccupation with the theme of martyrdom need, however, to be understood in relationship to *The Spiritual Exercises*, written by St. Ignatius Loyola (Rome, 1548).[8] This text served as one of the major foundations of Jesuit activity. *The Spiritual Exercises* were not intended for wide publication, but were written for the benefit of young Jesuit novices.[9] In the text, the young initiate is called upon to meditate upon a series of religious topics, such as the Passion of Christ. More importantly, however, the Jesuit is asked to develop his "powers of imagining," which consist of exercising his sensuous capacities in order to reenact the lives and events of Christ's life described in the text.[10] At the simplest level, those practicing the exercises would call to mind the physical setting in which a given event took place, or what Ignatius called "an imaginative representation" of the place. For example, the reader would try to imagine the road from Bethany to Jerusalem on which Christ traveled toward his passion, the room in which he held his last supper, the garden in which he was betrayed, the house in which Mary his mother waited after the Crucifixion. Hearing, taste, smell, and touch were also called upon to enhance this living experience of the text.

The popularity of the martyrdom theme in early Jesuit art is thus related to the emphasis placed upon experiencing the spiritual exercises. A major tactic of the Jesuits in revitalizing the Catholic church was to revive the religious fervor of the early Christian period. The model Christian from this early stage of church history was the martyr, who following the example of Christ, was willing to spill his blood for his faith. The Jesuit colleges in Rome served as training grounds for martyrs, and the young men that entered these colleges were sent out to do missionary work, where they placed their lives at risk. Thus, Jesuit missionary work afforded young men the opportunity to themselves reenact the lives of Christ and early Christian martyrs. The "power of imagining" that was put into play in experiencing the spiritual exercises was no less than a preliminary step in constructing a living Christian experience.

II. The Role of Pictures in Jesuit Religious Experience

For St. Ignatius Loyola pictures played an important role in his experiential approach to religious life. The *Evangelicae historiae imagines (Commentaries on the Gospels)* [cat. no. 36], published in Antwerp in 1595/6, was a book combining text and images that had been commissioned by St. Ignatius.[11] Consisting of the Gospel texts illustrated with 153 images, the book was used to imbue young Jesuits in a habit of prayer that was closely tied to visual material. Pictures here were called upon to assist the reader in his meditations on the text. This relationship of pictures to text was in turn based on the "composition of place," or mental reconstruction of events recommended by St. Ignatius in *The Spiritual Exercises*. We are, in fact, told by Father Bartolomeo Ricci in the prologue to his *Vita D.N. Iesu Christi* of 1607 that despite St. Ignatius' exceptional gift for meditation, "whenever he was going to meditate on those mysteries of Our Saviour, shortly before his prayer he looked at the pictures that he had collected and displayed around his room for this purpose."[12]

The didactic intent and format of the *Evangelicae historiae imagines* were employed in the scenes of martyrdom depicted in Jesuit establishments in Rome. Notably, these scenes, in which the gruesome aspects of martyrdom were painted in great detail, were accompanied by didactic texts. In 1604, Louis Richeôme, a French Jesuit in Rome, published a book in Lyon, entitled, *La peinture spirituelle*, in which he takes the reader through all the pictures in S. Andrea and in the neighboring church of S. Vitale, and then guides him among the birds and flowers of the Novitiate garden.[13] His purpose was to provoke intense and "living" meditation on religious topics. According to Richeôme, extravagant pomp and the decorative aspects of painting were unimportant; instead, ". . . attention must be concentrated exclusively on the subject matter of the frescoes, which should be read like a sermon, more effective because paint lasted and words vanished."[14]

The theme of martyrdom continued to be employed in the decoration of Jesuit establishments. The painted decorations in the Gesù in Rome included numerous scenes of the martyrdom of early Christian saints, and Rubens' paintings for the aisles and galleries in the Jesuit church in Antwerp also included martyred saints.[15] The lives of early Christian martyrs were held before young Jesuits as a paradigm for the ideal Christian, and fittingly their missionary effort allowed them to actually become saints. In this process of negotiating Christian past and present, pictures played a crucial role.

Attached to the preoccupation among Jesuits with the theme of martyrdom was an inherent concern with the didactic propensities of the visual arts. This preoccupation with didactic images can explain the popularity that emblems had in Jesuit circles.[16] Emblem books, consisting of pictures combined with learned aphorisms, emerged in the sixteenth century, combining humanist erudition with didactic purpose.[17] The texts of emblem books were geared towards moral improvement, and the associated pictures served to make them more accessible. Emblem books also helped to further the Ignatian technique of appplying the senses to help the imagination picture in minutest detail the circumstances of religious import: the horror of sin, the torments of Hell, the delights of a pious life. In the *Emblemata sacra S. Stephani Coelii Montis intercolumnis affixa* (Rome, 1589), followed by *Triumphus Martyrum*, which contains reproductions of gruesome frescoes in the Jesuit church of S. Stefano Rotondo, one is told that the emblems were "sweet honey which was spread on the brim of the martyr's cup."[18] Pictures and text combine here to prepared the souls of the novices for the terrible trials which awaited them in their missions among the heathen.

III. Jesuit Interpretations of Conventional Christian Iconography

The didactic mode of reading pictures developed in scenes of martyrdom and in emblem literature informed the representation of religious history in Jesuit churches. Scenes from the life of Christ played, understandably, an important role in Jesuit imagery. In the Gesù in Rome, the title church of the order, scenes of *The Crucifixion* and *The Resurrection* were depicted over the two transept altars. The *Pietá* [cat. no. 10] by Scipione Pulzone, included in this exhibition, was also commissioned as an altarpiece for the Gesù. Rubens' ceiling paintings for the Jesuit church in Antwerp included scenes depicting *The Nativity, The Temptation of Christ, The Last Supper, The Crucifixion,* and *The Ascension of Christ*. The Jesuit college at S. Stefano Rotondo in Rome, contained a *Crucifixion*, its didactic intentions clearly evident in the text included in the painting.[19]

The predilection among Jesuits for scenes of Christ's Passion needs to be understood in relationship to the *Spiritual Exercises,* where the entire third week is given to this aspect of Christ's life.[20] Scenes from the Passion of Christ ought also be understood in relationship to the renewed importance of the Eucharist among members of the Society of Jesus.

Devotion to Christ's name originated in the fifteenth century, and perhaps even earlier. In the seventeenth century the practice spread by way of the Company of Jesus, whose title church in Rome, the Gesù, was dedicated to that holy name.[21] The emblem designating this devotion was the monogram "IHS," surrounded by rays of light and often enriched by images or symbols of Christ's five wounds.[22] Appropriately then, the ceiling nave in the Gesù painted between 1674 and 1679 by the Italian artist Giovanni Battista Gaulli, had as its central image the name of Jesus emerging from a dazzling sun, from which emanate the shafts of salvation represented as beams of radiant light.[23] This Jesuit emblem can be seen in numerous works included in the present exhibition. It is also the subject of a drawing by Gregorio de Ferrari [cat. no. 18].

Devotion to the name of Jesus also explains why Christ's circumcision was of interest to Jesuits.[24] Earlier, a relatively minor theme in Christian art, the circumcision of Christ emerged as one of the most important themes in Jesuit iconography.[25] This theme was of interest because it was at the moment of his circumcision that Christ was named. The practice of commissioning paintings depicting the circumcision for the high altar was followed in many Jesuit churches; notably the circumcision was the subject of Girolamo Muziano's painting for the High Altar in the Gesù. The illustration on display from Pozzo's *Perspectiva Pictorum et Architectorum Andreae Putei* [cat. no. 38] shows the related architectural design for the High Altar. Finally, paintings of the circumcision appeared in clandestine Jesuit chapels in seventeenth-century Holland. Leonaert Bramer, a Dutch artist who is represented in this exhibition in a painting depicting *The Glorification of Christianity* [cat. no. 1], depicted the circumcision on repeated occasions.

In Rubens' ceiling paintings for the Jesuit church in Antwerp, one painting depicts the name of Jesus [cat. no. 33], but it is significant that the name of Mary is also included in this cycle. Devotion to Mary was of prime importance in Jesuit practice, and this perhaps explains why Rubens included in his picture cycle other scenes from the Virgin's life. As a response to those Protestant reformers who, in the words of Emile Mâle, "took away from the Virgin all beauty, all poetry, all greatness," the Jesuits considered Mary to be patroness and joint author of their order.[26] In the *Imago primi saeculi Societatis Iesu* (Antwerp, 1640) [cat. no. 37] included in the exhibition, the Virgin is described as "nutrix, patrona, imo altera velut auctor Societatis."[27] The "Coronation of the Virgin," by Rubens in the Jesuit church in Antwerp, which also appears in the upper heavens in Leonaert Bramer's *Glorification of Christianity,* had a long tradition in Catholic iconography as an allegory of "the Church."[28]

Other types of imagery that had a long history in Christian art came to have special relevance among the Jesuits. The Church Fathers, whose writings were the foundation of the Catholic faith, had widespread popularity in the Counter-Reformation, and were invoked in reference to the Catholic fight against heresy. In Rubens' painting of *The Victory of St. Athanasius over the Arch-heretic Arius* in the Jesuit church in Antwerp, an allusion is made to the battle waged by Ignatius against Luther. The four Latin Church Fathers figure prominently in the foreground of Leonaert Bramer's *Glorification of Christianity* and were also painted on the pendentives of the dome of the Gesù. Rubens' ceiling paintings for the Jesuit church in Antwerp include both the four Latin and four Greek Fathers of the Church.

The Old Testament scenes represented by Rubens in his ceiling paintings for the Jesuit church in Antwerp [see cat. nos. 27-30] constitute an interesting chapter in the evolution of a distinctively Jesuit iconography.[29] Nine scenes from the Old Testament are here paired together with nine scenes from the New Testament. In this pairing of type and anti-type we may recognize the symbolic method made popular in the fourteenth and fifteenth centuries by two illustrated books, the *Biblia pauperum* and the *Speculum humane salvationis.* This is a rare instance within Jesuit iconography, where the Old Testament plays a part in legitimizing Catholicism.

The Jesuit concern with the didactic potential of pictures is also evident in the arena of seventeenth-century humanism. During this period the Jesuits were largely responsible for the education of the elite in Catholic Europe. Attuned more than any other religious order in this period to the didactic value of pictures, they often commissioned painted enigmas, which were visual riddles for students to solve.[30] The typical enigma would be a more or less straightforward representation of a scene from sacred, secular or mythological history, but one in which a practised mind could find hidden reference to some object, quite distinct from the apparent subject. For example, a picture of *Esther and Ahasuerus,* such as the one included in this exhibition [J. Punt, after P. P. Rubens, cat. no. 30], might be explained as a rainbow, caused by the refraction of the sun's rays on a cloud: the king on his throne symbolizes the sun, the sceptre with which he touches Esther the sun's rays, Esther herself, probably leaning backwards in a swoon, is the rainbow, and the women supporting her are the clouds.[31] Such visual games could help in the memorization of scenes of religious significance.[32]

IV. Jesuit Iconography and the Jesuit Enterprise

The evolution of Jesuit imagery from the late-sixteenth through the mid-eighteenth century may be divided into two stages. In the earliest phase of Jesuit church decoration, martyrdoms constituted the preferred subject matter of paintings. This was complemented by a renewed concern with other traditional Catholic themes, such as the circumcision of Christ, to which a new Jesuit interpretation was added. During the 1620s, however, a major transformation in the orientation of Jesuit imagery came about when Ignatius Loyola and Francis Xavier were canonized. Following this, Jesuit imagery became preoccupied with its contemporary heroes and with celebrating Jesuit achievements.

As the founder of the Jesuit order, St. Ignatius Loyola came to have a special status in Jesuit imagery.[33] As works included in the present exhibition demonstrate, Ignatius was depicted in a variety of ways. One of the most well-known works depicting Ignatius is Rubens' altarpiece for the Jesuit church in Antwerp. Here, the founder of the order appears within an imposing church, exorcizing demons and healing the sick. Other popular images of Ignatius include his "Glorification," and portraits of him, either alone, or surrounded by companions. He appears in this exhibition in a bronze relief by an unidentified Roman master, depicting *St. Ignatius Surrounded by his Jesuit Companions* [cat. no. 12] and in Felix Anton Scheffler's drawing of *St. Ignatius and the Four Parts of the World: Allegory of Jesuit Missionary Work* [cat. no. 22].

The second most important figure in Jesuit imagery was Francis Xavier, most famous of Jesuit missionaries.[34] A second altarpiece by Rubens for the Jesuit church in Antwerp depicting "the Apostle of the Indies" performing miracles among the heathen. An altar in the Gesù contained a painting by Gaulli depicting the *Death of St. Francis Xavier.* In the present exhibition, works are included which depict this scene and other aspects of his missionary life. In a drawing by Marco Benefial [cat. no. 13] he is shown preaching to the Japanese, while in a drawing by Giuseppe Cades [cat. no. 15], he is shown embarking for India.

Next to St. Ignatius Loyola and St. Francis Xavier, St. Francis Borgia (1510-1572), St. Aloysius (or Louis) Gonzaga (1568-1591), and St. Stanislas Kotska (1550-1568) were the most commonly depicted figures in Jesuit imagery. Borgia was the Society's third Father General and played an important role in the evolution of the Jesuit order in Spain.[35] He appears in this exhibition in works depicting the moment of his conversion *(St. Francis Borgia Kneeling before the Body of Queen Isabella of Spain,* attributed to Palomino, [cat. no. 7], and he is also represented here in a statue by an unidentified Roman artist [cat. no. 11], intended for placement near an altarpiece in a Jesuit church.

St. Aloysius Gonzaga died at the age of twenty-three while serving the plague-stricken.[36] He appears in the present exhibition as the subject of an altarpiece for the Roman church of S. Ignazio by the Jesuit artist, Andrea Pozzo [cat. no. 19], and in glory in a painting attributed to the Italian artist, Francesco de Mura [cat. no. 6].

Saint Stanislas Kotska, who died at eighteen, had been a Jesuit novice for less than a year.[37] In this short time, however, his dedication to the Society earned him his saintly status. He also appears in the present exhibition in a drawing by Ciro Ferri, depicting him in ecstasy [cat. no. 17].

While individual Jesuit deeds were represented in paintings depicting Jesuit saints, there were also occasions on which the entire Jesuit cause was celebrated through the use of allegory. The most famous instance of this is the ceiling painting by the Jesuit, Andrea Pozzo, for the nave of S. Ignazio in Rome. This large fresco depicts *The Triumph of the Society of Jesus* (1691-94). In the year of its completion the painter himself elucidated the theme of this painting in a letter to the Prince of Lichtenstein, stating that the idea was taken from the verse in St. Luke: "I have come to bring fire upon earth," to which S. Ignatius replied, "Go and light the flame over the world."[38] In this painting the sky opens to reveal God the Father, the Son and the Holy Ghost bearing the cross. The flame of Charity and Faith passes from Father to Son, from Son to St. Ignatius, from St. Ignatius to his disciples, and from this to the entire world. Disposed around the painted architecture are personifications of Europe, Asia, Africa, and America, all bearing witness to the accomplishments of the order, and crushing the heretics beneath their feet. The painting depicts the triumph of Loyola's apostolate on earth, and at the same time is an allegory of the Jesuit missionary effort. Felix Anton Scheffler's *St. Ignatius and the Four Parts of the World: Allegory of the Jesuit Missionary Work* [cat. no. 22], included in the exhibition, is based on Pozzo's painting.

The transition within Jesuit imagery from a preoccupation with scenes of martyrdom and early Christian and biblical imagery in the early stages of development to scenes celebrating individual Jesuits, as well as the entire Jesuit enterprise, at a later stage, is a key issue in the evolution of Jesuit art. This transition is not only evident in paintings, prints and drawings, but also in comparing two of the printed volumes included in the exhibition.

The *Evangelicae historiae imagines* [cat. no. 36], published in Antwerp in 1595/6, contains 153 engravings illustrating the Gospels read at the Mass on Sundays.[39] This volume clearly belongs to the first stage of Jesuit iconography. Lettered captions appear underneath each engraving, corresponding to letters of the alphabet placed near the incidents depicted in the engravings. The second part of the book consists of learned exegetical annotations about each lettered incident, followed finally by a meditation or prayer. Pictorial imagery functions in accordance with the value placed upon pictures by St. Ignatius; it is entirely devoted to steering the reader to a vivid and personal understanding of the text.

In the *Imago primi saeculi Societatis Iesu* [cat. no. 37], published in Antwerp in 1640, the Jesuit order has itself become a central focus.[40] This magnificent volume was produced by the Jesuits of Antwerp to mark the centenary of the approval of their statutes. Text and allegorical pictures triumphantly proclaim Jesuit success. Whereas the 1595/6 volume was addressed primarily to young Jesuit novices, this volume was an attempt to legitimize the Jesuit enterprise to the world at large.

Jesuit imagery in its earlier stages was strongly didactic, but starting in the 1620s its didacticism relaxed in the wake of other more pressing concerns. Remarkably successful, but at the same time constantly under attack in the course of the seventeenth century, Jesuit imagery became progressively preoccupied with the Jesuit enterprise itself. Jesuit art from the 1620s onward reveals itself straightforwardly as an art of "legitimacy," celebrating as it does Jesuit heroes and the Jesuit enterprise at large. But even earlier, we may also encounter Jesuit art as legitimizing a particular cause. The Jesuits arose as a militant order, dedicated to the principles of the Counter-Reformation church, intent upon combating heresy. Early Jesuit imagery, consisting as it does of martyrdoms, mostly of early Christian saints, as well as other elements of early Christian history, is overtly an art of legitimacy, intent in this case upon validating Catholicism.

To understand the way in which Jesuit imagery shifted from a broad concern with church history, to a narrower concern with its own successes and survival is to touch upon the history of the order itself. From the official papal approval of the order in 1540, to its suppression in 1773, Jesuit history is marked by a series of triumphs and setbacks. Notably, Pozzo's fresco celebrating the Jesuit missionary effort was created following a period of Jesuit glory, but also just prior to the moment that decline began to set in. Heinrich Scherer's map of China, discussed in J. B. Harley's essay, translates Pozzo's allegory of conquest to a mission achieved precisely in the period when Jesuit influence began to decline.

An overview of Jesuit iconography demonstrates its underlying unity. Despite the transformation from imagery celebrating good Christians to imagery celebrating good Jesuits, Jesuit iconography remains consistent in its concern with legitimizing an enterprise that is under attack. While conforming in this way to Counter-Reformation imagery as a whole, Jesuit iconography can be understood and appreciated for the distinct and unique contribution that it made to a vibrant era in the visual arts.

NOTES

1. While no comprehensive study of Jesuit iconography exists, the subject has been discussed in general iconographical studies of the period. See, for instance, Emile Mâle, *L'art religieux après le Concile de Trente* (Paris: A colin, 1932); Mario Praz, *Studies in Seventeenth-Century Imagery*, 2 vols. (Rome: Edizioni di Storia e Letteratura, 1964); John B. Knipping, *Iconography of the Counter Reformation in the Netherlands* (Leiden: B. de Graff-Nieuwkoop/ A. W. Sijthoff, 1974). See also, John R. Martin, *The Ceiling Paintings for the Jesuit Church in Antwerp* I, Corpus Rubenianum Ludwig Burchard (Brussels: Arcade Press, 1968); Joan Evans, *Monastic Iconography in France from the Renaissance to the Revolution* (Cambridge: Cambridge University Press, 1970); *Saint, Site, and Sacred Strategy: Ignatius, Rome, and Jesuit Urbanism*, T. M. Lucas, S.J. ed. (Rome: Biblioteca Apostolica Vaticana, 1990).

2. On the theme of martyrdom, see, Howard Hibbard, "*Ut picurae sermones:* The First Painted Decorations of the Gesù," in *Baroque Art: The Jesuit Contribution*, ed. Rudolf Wittkower and Irma Jaffe (New York: Fordham University Press, 1972); Thomas Buser, "Jerome Nadal and Early Jesuit Art in Rome," *The Art Bulletin* 58, (1976) 424-433; David Freedberg, "The Representation of Martyrdoms during the Early Counter Reformation in Antwerp," *Burlington Magazine* 117, (1976) 128-138; Leif H. Monssen, "*Rex Gloriose Martyrum:* A Contribution to Jesuit Iconography," *The Art Bulletin* 63, (1981) 130-137.

3. S. Andrea al Quirinale was commissioned by Cardinal Camillo Pamphili for the novices of the Jesuit Order. See, R. Wittkower, *Art and Architecture in Italy, 1600-1750* (London: Penguin Books, 1965) 119-121.

4. Discussion of the painted decorations for St. Thomas of Canterbury can be found in Buser, "Jerome Nadal," 429-432. The paintings were executed by the Italian artist, Niccolò Circignani. The frescoes are based on engravings included in a book on Catholic martyrs in England by Cardinal William Allen, the leader of the Catholic Church in exile. Circignani's frescoes for St. Thomas of Canterbury were engraved by G. B. Cavaleriis (Rome, 1584).

5. S. Stefano Rotondo was an early Christian temple given to the German college by Pope Gregory XIII. The rector commissioned Nicolò Circignani to paint a series of frescoes depicting the martyrdoms of early Christian saints mostly enacted under the late Roman empire. They were deliberately painted in great detail; the explanation of each torture was attached to each fresco. See Haskell, *Patrons and Painters*, 65-66; Buser, "Jerome Nadal," 428; Monssen, "*Rex Gloriose Martyrum*"; Lucas, *Saint, Site, and Sacred Strategy*.

6. See Lucas, *Saint, Site and Sacred Strategy*, 50.

7. For discussion of the religious Orders in relationship to artistic patronage, see Haskell, *Patrons and Painters*, 63-93.

8. See Antonio De Nicolás, *Powers of Imagining* (New York: State University of New York Press, 1986) for a modern interpretation of this text. De Nicolás recovers the radical flavor of *The Spiritual Exercises* by placing it within the old tradition of mnemonics or the cultivation of memory.

9. Young Jesuit novices did not actually themselves read *The Spiritual Exercises*, rather this text was presented to them under the guidance of a Novice Master.

10. See De Nicolas, *Powers of Imagining* for discussion of this concept in *The Spiritual Exercises*.

11. This publication is the focus of discussion of Jesuit art in T. Buser, "Jerome Nadal."

12. See Buser, "Jerome Nadal," 425.

13. See Evans, *Monastic Iconography*, 46 and Haskell, *Patrons and Painters*, 67-68. S. Vitale, an early Christian church, was given to the Jesuits by Pope Gregory XIII.

14. Louis Richeôme, *Le peinture spirituelle* (Lyon: 1611) 21.

15. See Hibbard, "*Ut picturae sermones*" for a discussion of the early painted decorations for the Gesù and Martin, *Ceiling Paintings* for discussion of Rubens' ceiling paintings and altarpieces for the Jesuit church in Antwerp.

16. On Jesuits and emblem books, see Praz, *Studies*, 170-199.

17. The emblematic concept arose through the attempts of Italian humanists to create a modern equivalent to the Egyptian hieroglyph. Its background was Renaissance Platonism, which laid stress on the visual image as a vehicle for hidden philosphic mysteries. The emblem book was a literary genre which enjoyed its heyday in the sixteenth and seventeenth centuries. The emblem book was part of that vast codification of symbolism which led to Cesare Ripa's *Iconologia* (1593).

18. Praz, *Studies*, 171.

19. This painting is the subject of an article by Monssen, "*Rex Gloriose Martyrum*."

20. See Martin, *Ceiling Paintings*, 196.

21. See Knipping, *Iconography*, 110.

22. "IHS" are the first three letters of Iesus in Greek.

23. See Ebria Feinblatt, "Jesuit Ceiling Decoration," *The Art Quarterly* X, 4 (Autumn, 1947) 245.

24. On the importance of this theme in Jesuit iconography, see, Evans, *Monastic Iconography*, 48-49; Hibbard, "*Ut picturae sermones*," 32-33; Cornelis Goossens, "Nog meer over David Vinckboons," *Jaarboek van Het Koninklijk Museum voor Schone Kunsten te Antwerpen*, (1966) 59-106.

25. The feast of the circumcision on January 1 was, and is, the titular feast of the Society of Jesus, and was celebrated with special pomp in Jesuit churches.

26. See Mâle, *L'art religieux*, 30.

27. *Imago primi saeculi Societatis Iesu* (Antwerp: Officina Plantiniana, 1640) 72.

28. See Mâle, *Religious Art in France: The Thirteenth Century* (Princeton: Princeton University Press, 1984) 255-256.

29. See J. Patrice Marandel in the present catalogue for consideration of the unusual nature of Old Testament imagery in a Jesuit church.

30. See Jennifer Montagu, "The Painted Enigma and French Seventeenth-Century Art," *Journal of the Warburg and Courtauld Institutes* 31, (1968) 307-335.

31. See C. F. Menestrier, *La philosophie des images énigmatiques* (Lyons: 1694) 27.

32. For a discussion of the importance of "memory" in Jesuit religious experience, see De Nicolàs, *Powers of Imagining* and Jonathan D. Spence, *The Memory Place of Matteo Ricci* (New York: Randam House, 1984). Matteo Ricci (1552-1610) was one of the most important missionaries in China. He taught the Chinese how to build a memory palace, an imaginary place in the mind for the storage and retrieval of images.

33. See Joseph N. Tylenda, S.J., *Jesuit Saints and Martyrs* (Chicago: Loyola University Press, 1984) 241-250.

34. See Tylenda, *Jesuit Saints*, 449-454.

35. See Tylenda, *Jesuit Saints*, 352-255.

36. In 1605 the ecclesiastical authorities permitted the faithful to invoke Aloysius of Gonzaga as being "blessed." A year later his spiritual director wrote his biography, which within ten years appeared in Antwerp in a Netherlandish translation, illustrated with copper engravings by Jan Collaert. See Tylenda, *Jesuit Saints*, 190-193.

37. See Tylenda, *Jesuit Saints*, 401-404. Engravings by Anton Wierix and Schelte à Bolswert show him kneeling in adoration before the Host in a monstrance.

38. See Feinblatt, "Jesuit Ceiling Decoration," 246.

39. This volume is discussed in Buser, "Jerome Nadal," and Praz, *Studies*, 185-189.

40. This publication is discussed in Knipping, *Iconography*, 143-44.

The Role of Images in Jesuit Churches: Two Examples

J. Patrice Marandel

I.

With the bull "Regimini Militantis," Pope Paul III Farnese, recognizing the merits of the society founded by Ignatius of Loyola, confirmed in 1540 its establishment as a religious order. Obviously, the new and still numerically small order, which had been active in Rome for only two years, did not have at its disposal a proper place of worship. The same year, however, one of its members, Ignatius's first Italian recruit, Pietro Codacio da Lodi, obtained the right to use a small church called Santa Maria della Strada, which the Pope subsequently officially granted to the newly-established order.

The church was well-located in the center of Rome, thus inaugurating the traditional concern of the Jesuits to site their churches in the very hearts of cities. The small parish given in 1540 to the Jesuits was close to the Pope's residence, as it was to the nerve center of the Roman government and to the residential as well as popular neighborhoods.

The particular benevolence of the Papacy toward the establishment of the Jesuits was due to several historical factors: the development of Protestantism throughout Europe, which caused serious concern to Rome, and the sack of Rome in 1527 by the armies of Charles V.[1] These events had prompted a need for reaffirming and for reforming dogmas and liturgy, which eventually found their formalization in the decisions of the Council of Trent (which was convoked in 1536 and held after 1545).

In his insightful essay on the building of the Gesù, James Ackerman has explained how the need for liturgical reforms, and the role imparted to the Jesuits in their implementation, was decisive in the design of the church.[2] Work on a new church, much needed to replace the small chapel of Santa Maria della Strada, did not begin until 1550. From the earliest known project for the church, by Nanni di Baccio Bigio[3] to the one promoted by Alessandro Cardinal Farnese, and eventually adopted by Vignola, a major concern dominated the enterprise: that of creating a church that would be practical and suited to the needs of the Order.[4] Hence, for instance, the often noted decision to install a flat roof that would help the acoustics and make the sermons more intelligible to the worshippers. Aesthetic considerations which led to the hiring of Vignola were, it seems, of little interest to the Jesuits. These battles were fought at the level of the patrons who were paying for the building. The design of the Gesù, although modern and different from "traditional" churches, was not as innovative as it has often been said. Ackerman has demonstrated that the demands made on architects by the liturgical reforms of the late sixteenth century, which included, for instance, a need for repeated, indeed simultaneous, celebrations of Mass, had already been articulated in the design of smaller churches, or by Northern Italian architects in the years just preceding the planning of the Gesù and its construction.

The original spirit of the Counter-Reformation called for great austerity in the design of church interiors, a fact not sufficiently noted. This austerity is opposed to our common conception which associates the art of the Counter-Reformation with the ornate "Baroque" style. Thus Francesco Grigi, a Venetian Franciscan, wrote in 1535: ". . . I should like to have it (the ceiling of new churches) coffered with . . . squares . . . treated in a workmanlike manner with gray paint."[5] It is also sufficient, as Ackerman reminds us, to consider the stark interior of Palladio's San Giorgio Maggiore (1568) to understand this tendency in the design of church interiors and to dissipate the facile equation too often established between the Counter-Reformation and the proliferation of images.

Considering the rich decorations which adorn the Gesù as we know it today, it is indeed hard to reconcile the recommendations for simplicity in design of Counter-Reformers, such as St. Charles Borromeo (*Instruc-*

tionum Fabricae et Supellectis Ecclesiasticae libri duo, 1577) with the way the church has developed through the centuries.[6]

Authors concur that originally, painted decorations were not essential to the Order. In the words of R. Wittkower: "the Society had scarcely any aesthetic ambitions before 1600 . . ."[7] This harsh statement can, perhaps, be somewhat softened if one considers the conditions surrounding the artistic development of the church. First of all, as noted by Francis Haskell, the Jesuits had to accept the overwhelming presence of Alessandro Cardinal Farnese.[8] This enlightened prelate, who had succeeded in imposing his preferred architect, wished at the time to control the painted decorations of the church. His selection of painters may have been guided by the relative scarcity of first-rate artists in Rome at the time. In any case, it fell short of its goal. Girolomo Muziano, for instance, was given the exacting task to create the major painting in the church, the *Circumcision* for the high altar.[9] Sydney Freedberg has observed that "the impression his works make is not just a function of the grand scale of their forms, nor of the evident power that inhabits their restraint, but of the oppressive melancholy in Counter-Reformation spirituality that Muziano conveys to us,"[10] noting also that "boredom is a requisite of the Roman Counter-Maniera."[11] Giovanni de'Vecchi may have started more spirited work on the pendentives and the dome, but this work stopped short at the time of Alessandro Farnese's death in 1589. The chapels on either side of the nave had been adopted by various families who, acting as patrons, commissioned their preferred (or available) artists to decorate them. The juxtaposition of paintings by Hans von Aachen, Francesco Bassano, Scipione Pulzone [cat. n. 10], Agostino Ciampelli, and Federigo Zuccari did not create an homogeneous ensemble nor did it create—in spite of the individual achievements of these artists—a very distinguished group of paintings.

This peculiar mixture of paintings which are stylistically unrelated is the best argument against the idea that a "Jesuit style" was formulated shortly after the establishment of the order, and that it was imposed on other churches, not only in Rome but throughout the world as well. It is difficult to determine if the order played in fact any part at all in the choice of the artists, or even if they were approved by the church authorities beyond their credibility as artists adequately able to transpose into images current, Counter-Reformation, subjects. In this respect, the choice of the Jesuit painter Giuseppe Valeriano to decorate two chapels in the Gesù—the Cappella della Madonna della Strada and the Cappella della Passione—is both relevant and appropriate. A singularly uninspired painter, Valeriano can be located stylistically between Muziano and Pulzone (who was Valeriano's assistant for the Cappella della Strada). The only merit of his compositions is to affect an almost naive simplicity that confers on them an immediate and effective legibility. The substance of the message implied in these images was for Valeriano evidently more important than the elaboration of a visual language. His paintings appeal directly to the emotions of a simple viewer. They are true objects of devotion. Fortunately, Valeriano's simple-minded formulas were never promoted—in spite of his position within the order—as official Jesuit art. It is to the credit of the Society to have in effect promptly rejected such banal style, and to have thus avoided aesthetic banality for centuries.

Given the haphazard nature of the first round of decorations for the Gesù, and the random choice of artists, it is amazing to realize that some unity was maintained in the project through the establishment of an iconongraphic program. Howard Hibbard has stressed with eloquence, and for the first time, the ties that link the nave chapels of the Gesù to one another, and their relationship to the high and transept altars.[12] Hibbard argues that this program, pairing chapels thematically, may have originated in the early planning stages of the church, and could perhaps be credited to Francis Borgia himself. Coming from the entrance, the first two chapels on either side of the nave are devoted to martyrdom and preaching, two "vocations" of the Jesuits; the central chapels are in turn devoted to the two poles of Christ's life: His Nativity and His Passion; the two chapels closer to the choir are dedicated to the realm of Heaven: the Trinity on one side, Angels on the other. Finally, in the transept, the Crucifixion and Resurrection (Christ as Redeemer) flanked the Circumcision on the tribune-an appropriate image that celebrated the naming of Christ and by extension the order that bore His name.

The originality of the program is noted by Hibbard, who comments that no other church built in Rome at the time offered such a "reading." If there is a Jesuit art, it is certainly more in this kind of manipulation of images to serve spiritual goals than in matters of style that it can be found. How obvious this program was to the crowds that gathered in the Gesù remains to be studied. Did the sermons delivered there "walk" the listeners through the various representations of the altarpieces? If many worshippers may have missed the point, it is also probable that those more familiar with St. Ignatius' *Spiritual Exercises* responded to it. We would like to suggest also that the thematic organization of the Gesù may have shared something with religious theater. The *Theatrum sacrum* played an important role in the teachings of the Jesuits. Furthermore, the configuration of the chapels in the "theater of Faith" suggest also a familiarity with the Renaissance "memory theater," used to teach mnemonic techniques.[13] It has been pointed out that Ignatius himself was familiar with the work of Ramon Lull.[14] According to Taylor, "a possible influence of the art of memory with its emphasis on *"loci"* and *"images"* can be detected in the *Spiritual Exercises."*

Considering the originality of this design, one may wonder why this first scheme was so rapidly obliterated by changes and additions. First of all, as noted by art historians who have tried to reconstitute the original decoration of the Gesù, this one lacked the kind of cohesiveness that made it really effective. Francis Haskell suggests that the church may have looked "bleak."[15] Furthermore, aesthetics changed rapidly in seventeenth-century Rome. Some of the political, psychological, and spiritual forces which had prompted the Counter-Reformation, of which the establishment of the Jesuits and the building of their church in Rome were two manifestations, had changed. Rome had gotten over the trauma of its sack in 1527. The church, its spiritual as well as temporal power, seemed secure. Protestantism seemed confined essentially to the Northern countries, and did not present an immediate threat to the Papacy. The Jesuits themselves, while continuing their mission at home, became increasingly involved in the evangelization of distant countries. Their first martyrs were rapidly canonized. By 1622, Ignatius, and Francis Xavier had become saints, later followed by Francis Borgia and Stanislas Kostka. These new saints triggered new devotions among the faithful. The practical attitudes of the Jesuits toward aesthetic matters, which had allowed them to accept (rather than promote) the severe formulae of the Counter-Reformation—and which at the same time gave them great flexibility in the building of their colonial churches—made them also alter profoundly the design of the Roman establishments. Whether or not the original iconongraphic program of the early Gesù was still operative, there was no hesitation to transform the two chapels of the transept—originally dedicated to the Crucifixion and the Resurrection of Christ—into shrines honoring St. Ignatius and St. Francis Xavier. For the latter, the aging Pietro da Cortona designed an altar (1674-78) intended to frame Maratta's *Death of Francis Xavier*. For the former, the Jesuit artist Andrea Pozzo designed a formidable ensemble (1696-1700), the realization of which was given to some of the greatest sculptors of the time, including Alessandro Algardi and Pierre Legros.

In less than a century the success of the Jesuits had been astonishing. Now one of the most powerful orders in Italy, their contribution to the Christian faith throughout the world was incontestable. The "new" iconography of the Roman Jesuit churches culminating with Gaulli's work at the Gesù (1675-1685),[16] and Pozzo's ceiling at St. Ignatius, marked the apotheosis of the order.

II.

There seems to have been an attempt on the part of the Jesuits to codify their artistic standards for the building of their churches. Father Giuseppe Valeriano offered to write a treatise on the subject, but his project was abandoned by 1580. By then many churches were either planned or in progress throughout Europe. How much the Roman Gesù served as a model remains conjectural. The case of the Jesuit church in Antwerp is of considerable interest in this respect.

The church planned by the Jesuits for the city of Antwerp was to become the most important Jesuit monument in Northern Europe. Its partial destruction by fire in 1718 meant the loss of one of Rubens' most important decorative cycles. Yet, enough is known today about the church itself to make a discussion of the building relevant in the context of this essay.[17]

Although the Gesù participated fully in the movement of the Roman Counter-Reformation, its building and decoration took place long enough after the sack of Rome in 1527 to reflect an aspect of Jesuit pietism that is more mystical than militant. Only with the accomplishments—mostly abroad—of the Company did the decoration of the Gesù become, as we have shown, an image of the glorification of the order. In Antwerp instead, the Jesuits' firm establishment in the city preceded only by a few years the building of the new church. A Jesuit community had been established there in 1562, but in 1578 had been expelled by the Protestants. The capture of the city by Alessandro Farnese allowed the Jesuits to return to the city where they flourished until their expulsion in 1773.

The building of the church began in 1615 under the direction of a Jesuit architect, Pieter Huyssens (1577-1637).[18] The church knew none of the vicissitudes the Roman Gesù had experienced. Money had been raised by public subscription, and was at first plentiful. The architect was eventually scorned for his lavish expenses on the double count that the opulence of the church betrayed the spirit of poverty and, more practically, that it had created a heavy burden of debts. Jacobus Tirinus (1580-1636), who had been appointed superior in 1616, was eventually dismissed in 1625 because of the magnitude of the debts he incurred. There was, however, in the planning of the church no interference from higher authorities with the making of decisions. The construction took six years, its completion coinciding almost with the canonization of the first Jesuit saints. The original conception of the building "according to the rules of Vitruvius," and the use of "Ligurian marble" both contributed to its splendor and novelty within the context of Flemish architecture.[19] The façade in particular was an obvious reference to that of the Gesù in Rome, upon which it embroiders. The interior plan, however, differed greatly from the Roman church. It is that of an early Roman basilica with two two-story aisles. The ceiling of the nave was, according to Martin, "covered with a wooden tunnel vault all'antica, decorated with gilt coffering and rosettas," while those of the aisles and tribunes had flat ceilings.[20]

Unlike the decoration of the first Gesù, which happened randomly, the Jesuits in charge in Antwerp were more firmly decided on devising a unified decorative program for their church. An advantage they had over their earlier Roman counterparts was the domineering presence in Antwerp of Rubens, who returned to his native city from Italy in 1608. This artist was sympathetic to and had good relations with the Order. In 1613, he produced vignettes for the Opticorum libri sex of the Order's rector, Father Francois Aguilon. He also knew the architect of the Jesuit church, Huyssens, whom he helped with the design of decorative elements on the façade, and was equally well-connected with the powerful Tirinus, who signed the contract of agreement with Rubens. It was probably around 1615 that Rubens began work on two large altarpieces, which were shown in alternation in the church, The Miracles of St. Ignatius Loyola, and The Miracles of St. Francis Xavier. The mere fact that these two paintings were conceived before the canonization of the saints (that occurred only seven years later) demonstrated a familiarity between the artist and the order. Huyssens himself in designing a church with so many flat ceilings had certainly in mind to have them decorated, and most likely by Rubens, who may have been brought at an early date in the conception of the whole project.

The presence of one of Europe's greatest artists in their city, their ability to secure his participation, and the fact that, in contrast with the Gesù in Rome, the question of individual patronage never interfered with the general plan for the decoration of the church (the very architecture of the church prevented such interference), contributed to give the Antwerp church a homogeneity seldom achieved before or since.

In Antwerp, as in Rome, the painted decorations were part of an established program which delineated the position of the Jesuit establishment and its mission. At the time of the erection of the church, Antwerp had barely escaped Protestant rule. The reaffirmation of the presence of the Catholic church, and of the Jesuits, was thus perceived as a privileged Renaissance. The two altarpieces, commissioned before the ceiling decorations, present the two major saints of the Order not in their glory or at the time of their death, as they will be a few years later at the Gesù, but as thaumaturgists admired for their reputed healing miracles. Thus an equation was established between their lives and those of the apostles: the same way the apostles had established the church, the early Jesuits had regenerated it. By extension, their power over heresy was asserted. More complicated was the meaning and relationship of the thirty-nine ceiling paintings Rubens had to devise for the rest of the church (it should be noted that the execution of these ceilings was left largely to assistants, Van Dyck among them). It is not known if a single person was responsible for the program, which seems rather a compendium of Catholic—not purely Jesuit—themes. It is likely that Jacobus Tirinus was involved with it. Martin notes that the contract he signed with Rubens reserved him the right to make changes in the list of subjects, and also that he may have enlisted the help of Heribertus Rosweyde, a hagiographer appointed to the Jesuit College at Antwerp and the author, among other books, of a *Vitae Patrum* (1615). The two tiers of the church allowed for two separate ensembles, the lower one representing individual images of Church fathers and female saints around two allegories of the names of Jesus and Mary. If these represent typical subjects of Jesuit devotion, the litany of saints on either side of them does not. As Rubens was painting these representations, the prevalent iconography in Roman Jesuit churches was that of the Order's saints. In Antwerp there is a concerted effort to display a larger number of saints, Church Fathers and martyrs in particular. There is little doubt that this display of saints on the first level of the church—the one most accessible to the public and immediately seen—was an affirmation of the cult of the saints in the face of Protestantism. The representation of Church Fathers, who had fought heresies, acquired in this respect a special significance, while images of martyrs—even though female in this case—illustrated a direct link between the Jesuits and their mission.

The alternation of scenes from the Old and the New Testaments in the upper gallery was not an innovation in itself. For centuries Christian theologians had studied the Scriptures in order to find in both parts of the Bible types and antitypes which symbolically prefigured and completed one another. In late medieval times, and during the Renaissance, this type of dualism, and dualist imagery, had led to the publications of illustrated books, such as the *Biblia pauperum*. Emblem books, which acquired a growing importance among Jesuits, often used this device as well. Rubens, in fact, also used on occasion church images and symbols which had been popularized in emblem books.

The reference to the Old Testament is, however, fairly rare in Jesuit iconography. One may even cautiously wonder if, having addressed the Protestant heresy on the first level of the church, the intention was not on the upper one to stress the link between the Old Testament and its fulfillment in the New one as an affirmation of the Christian faith against the Hebraic tradition. Antwerp had already in the seventeenth century an important and highly visible Jewish community.

Unlike the reading of the iconographical program of the early Gesù, whose innovation, according to Hibbard, was to force the faithful to take into consideration at once chapels located on opposite sides of the nave, the one suggested in Antwerp would be more linear and could be followed almost like the pages of a book—something that is also dictated by the architecture of the church. The sequence begins on the left side with the *Fall of the Rebel Angels*, the first representation near the apse, and ends on the same side with *Moses in Prayer*. This last image is not paired with a scene from the New Testament, but the sequence resumes again with the *Crucifixion*, on the other side of the apse. To give an idea of the complexity of the iconographic program, it may be noted that this *Crucifixion* can on one hand be paired with the *Sacrifice of Isaac* which follows it. The parallel between the two subjects appears in the *Biblia pauperum*, an illustrated late medieval compendium of stories from the Old and New Testaments. On the other hand, it could also be related across the apse—and the altarpiece of one of the two Jesuit saints—to the *Fall of the Angels*, the three pictures forming in that case an illustration of Jesuit life, with its defeating of heresy and communion with Christ's sacrifice in martyrdom. Furthermore, looking down the aisle, the image next to the *Sacrifice of Isaac* was that of the *Resurrection*. The *Resurrection* and *Crucifixion* originally flanked the *Circumcision* in the Roman Gesù. Another interpretation of the *Sacrifice of Isaac* is that it was a prefiguration of Christ's circumcision.[24] These are perhaps fine points which, as in the Roman Gesù, would have escaped the casual worshipper in the church. But the Jesuit church at Antwerp and its *collegium* ranked among the most sophisticated religious institutions in the Christian world. Helped by the genius of Rubens, many of its visitors would have understood, that the role of these images was ultimately to celebrate the glory of Christ, of the Virgin Mary, and of the saints. And all would also have understood that the Jesuits, among all orders, were especially instrumental in fighting on earth for that celebration.

NOTES

1. Andre Chastel, *The Sack of Rome, 1527*, The A.W. Mellon lectures in the Fine Arts, Princeton, 1983.
2. James Ackerman, "The Gesù in the Light of Contemporary Church Design," in *Baroque Art: The Jesuit Contribution*, ed. by R. Wittkower and I. Jaffe, (New York, 1972).
3. *Ibid*, plate 7a.
4. *Ibid*, plate 8.
5. Quoted in Rudolf Wittkower, *Architectural Principles in the Age of Humanism* (London: 1949), 155 ff.
6. James Ackerman, *op. cit.*, 20, note 16.
7. Rudolf Wittkower, "Problems of the Theme," in *Baroque Art*, 8.
8. Francis Haskell, *Patrons and Painters*, London, 1963, 65.
9. On the novelty and significance of the subject, see June ten Brink-Goldsmith in the present catalogue.
10. Sidney Freedberg, *Painting in Italy, 1500-1600* (1975), 500.
11. *Ibid*, 499.
12. Howard Hibbard, "Ut picturae sermones: The First Painted Decoration of the Gesù," in *Baroque Art*, 29-49.
13. Frances A. Yates, *The Art of Memory* (London: 1966).
14. René Taylor, "Hermetism and Mystical Architecture," in *Baroque Art*, 65.
15. Francis Haskell, *op. cit.*, 66.
16. Karolina Lanckoronska, "Un monument artistique de la Contre-Reforme victorieuse," in *Actes du VIIe congrès international des sciences historiques* (Warsaw: 1935 (Vol. 1, 163-168; Robert Engass, *The Paintings of Baccicio* (University Park: 1964).
17. John Rupert Martin, *The Ceiling Paintings for the Jesuit Church in Antwerp*, Corpus Rubenianum Ludwig Burchard, Part I, (London and New York: 1968).
18. J. Braun, *Die belgischen Jesuitenkirchen* (Freiburg: 1907) 151-171.
19. Henschensius, *Acta Sanctorum Martii* 1, (1668) 24, quoted in John Rupert Martin, *The Ceiling Paintings*, 25.
20. John Rupert Martin, *The Ceiling Paintings*, 27.
21. *Lexikon der Christlichen Ikonographie*, Vol 1, ed. Engelbert Kirschbaum, S.J., (Freiburg: 1990), 271.

The Map as Mission: Jesuit Cartography as an Art of Persuasion

J. B. Harley

In the early fifteenth century Jacopo d' Angelo presented to Pope Alexander V the first Latin translation of Ptolemy's *Geographia*, and the dedication expressed the hope that the book would serve as "an announcement of his coming rule . . . so that he may know what vast power over the world he will soon achieve."[1] These words would have fitted equally well the Jesuit appreciation of cartography, for to them it was also an art of persuasion. Though cartography has not been systematically treated as an overall part of Jesuit history, it is clear that the Jesuits more than other religious orders of early modern Europe valued maps and geography for the control of missionary space.[2] In all the provinces where the Jesuits had missions—such as China, Japan, India, the United States, Canada, and South America—they have left a record in maps of their spiritual conquests. Many of these maps were merely filed in the archives, but others—transmitted through various channels to the map workshops of Italy, Germany, France, and the Low Countries—were published as often landmark contributions to the geographical image Europe held of the world at large. And not surprisingly, the first atlas of the Holy Land [1532] was by the German Jesuit, Jacob Ziegler. The sustained Jesuit interest in mapping, from the sixteenth to the eighteenth century, merits understanding at several levels.

That Jesuit cartography should have developed at all is linked to the training members of the order received in subjects that permitted them to make accurate geographical observations.[3] Mathematics and geography were a regular part of the curriculum in the Jesuit colleges. Jonathan Spence has remarked that "By placing emphasis on mathematical skills the Jesuits proved that they stood at the frontiers of modern knowledge and had inherited the dominant thrust of late Renaissance Italian humanism."[4] Jesuit learning—no less than secular learning—included astronomy, arithmetic, geometry, geography, and the study of spheres as well as training in the use of instruments such as the astrolabe and the quadrant. Taken together these disciplines provided many of the necessary skills for cartography.

Upon these theoretical foundations the Jesuits created a cartography that is an important dimension of their contribution to the visual arts. Maps were vital aids to priests dislocated in missions scattered in immense and little-known territories. Large-scale architectural plans were drafted as part of the process of designing churches and missionary stations. Small-scale maps recorded the location of the missions, set out the routes the preachers would take, located native populations, and established the boundaries of ecclesiastical administrative units. To map the land was to possess it, and maps became visible persuaders accompanying the letters and *Relations* that the Jesuit Fathers sent back to Europe. If the patrons and superiors of the order had not travelled to America and Asia themselves, then maps, as accepted surrogates of geographical reality, made the conquest believable. Not least, maps were also documents on which the order could lay down strategies of future territorial expansion.

In less well-developed areas of the world—for example in Canada and South America—the Jesuits were also explorers. Their mapping in these contexts, helping to open up new territories to settlement and economic exploitation, became part of a wider campaign of colonial promotion. The missions often benefited from royal patronage, and from motives of mercantile gain as much as religious piety these authorities contributed to their set-up costs in areas distant from Europe. In return, the Jesuits, by becoming mapmakers, by describing the geography and natural resources of the new lands, or by compiling glossaries of native languages, spearheaded the intellectual conquest of empire. By participating in the larger imperial discourse of European overseas expansion, the Jesuit presence is sometimes blurred; but their maps served as a graphic shorthand for a more universal articulation of territorial ambition.

On the periphery of New France, the Jesuit contribution to the exploration and mapping of the Great Lakes region was an especially crucial one.[5] Conversion and commerce went hand-in-hand and, in the mid-seventeenth century, the basic maps of the area were largely derived from missionary journeys or from Indian intelligence gathered by members of the Jesuit Order and their *donnés*. The names of the explorers and mapmakers of the Midwest—Allouez, Brébeuf, Chaumonot, Dablon, Jogues, Lalemant, Marquette, Rayambault—are also a roll call of the Jesuit Fathers.[6] By recording the geography of America at first hand, the Jesuits also provided the raw material of the maps published in France that would become standard throughout Europe for over a century and that would help several generation of immigrants to envision the potential of the New World in advance of their arrival.

In the history of Jesuit cartography it is dangerous to generalize from one period or place to another. Thus, the Jesuit mapping in China and Japan is very different from that in America. In these sophisticated civilizations of East Asia, the Jesuits encountered maps that were partly comparable to their own so that cartography entered the vocabulary of cross-cultural communication. In China, with Father Matteo Ricci as the principal intermediary, there occurred a remarkable exchange of geographical information through maps.[7] It has been suggested that in Ricci's map this aspect of "the civilisation of the Far West was for the first time meeting that of the Far East."[8] In one direction, the European world map "translated" by Ricci into Chinese (1602) gave educated Chinese and Japanese scholars a new and somewhat disturbing vision of the world (though its influence on the technical development of traditional cartography should not be exaggerated).[9] In the other direction, just as the Jesuits contributed to Chinese knowledge of the earth and heavens, so too they opened channels by which Chinese maps and geographical writings could shape European perceptions of China from the late-sixteenth century onward.[10]

While this conventional picture of cross-cultural exchange is not without truth, it involved more than solely an innocent intellectual encounter. It was not the primary aim of the Jesuit Fathers to teach Chinese and Japanese scholars the essentials of western cartography. Instead we can interpret Matteo Ricci's maps, like the clocks and other technological marvels that were carried to the Chinese court, as tools in the Jesuit art of persuasion, or what Jacques Gernet has described as an "enterprise of seduction."[11] Thus the world map of Ricci, with its projection and graticule of latitude and longitude, proclaimed the advanced nature of European science. It was designed to display the territorial power of the sovereigns who reigned in Christendom as well as to define the world (albeit without direct reference either to Islam or to the growing schisms in the Catholic church) that had been evangelized for the Christian God.[12] By impressing the Chinese with his map, as Spence puts it, "Matteo Ricci hoped to interest them in his culture; through interesting them in his culture he hoped to draw them to an interest in God."[13]

Taking a broader view, there is no distinctive Jesuit cartography in the manner that there is a distinctive Jesuit iconography.[14] Jesuit mapmakers employed the same instruments, techniques, and styles that were the common currency of a reformed cartography throughout early modern Europe. Yet this is to judge the maps only by a technical yardstick. What distinguishes them in the history of cartography is their religious motivation and the aspects of persuasion to which they were harnessed. It is also true that Jesuit maps of the non-European world were quickly assimilated into the mainstream of European printed cartography; once in that form they could again serve the missionary cause with equal effectiveness. The cartographic history of the Jesuit order thus enshrines an example of the constant appropriation and reappropriation of maps as a form of power-knowledge in European society. Maps acquired a different meaning and vitality depending in whose hands—whether sacred or secular—they were placed.

For the Jesuit Fathers cartography probably remained firmly linked to the space and time of their religious world. A final set of clues linking cartography to the visual discourse to which missionary art also belongs appears in the marginal pictures on many of the maps. This is far from being mere decoration, but rather these pictures should alert us to the rhetoric of every map. Through the use of religious motifs on the title pages of atlases and in map cartouches, the missionary role of cartography is consecrated. In Jesuit cartography we encounter the same specific iconography—with the frequent use of the monogram for the name of Jesus (IHS) and figures of martyrs and saints from Catholic and Jesuit history—as in Jesuit art as a whole. On the maps of Canada the subjects include the religious orders themselves, crosses, light radiating from heaven, and angels occasionally wearing an Indian headdress. Together these motifs convey the characteristic missionary tension between ethnocentricity and enlightenment as Christianity sought to push the heathen back into the wilderness. But as with all Jesuit endeavor this is not without sacrifice. On one seventeenth-century map of Canada—attributed to the Jesuit Bressani—the martyrdom of Fathers Brébeuf and Lalemant is shown.[15] The map, by projecting a pictorial representation of this event into the grid of Euclidean space, universalizes the theme of martyrdom. The territory of New France, including the Great Lakes region, has become the theater in which the forces of good and evil are playing for possession of the land. Through such scenes the unity of art and cartography is established. We are reminded that maps are a way of seeing—and an art of persuasion—that is as subjective as any painting. To grasp the historical meaning of Jesuit maps we must relate them to the wider ideology of the visual culture of the Counter-Reformation.

NOTES:

1. The dedication is found in the earliest Latin manuscript of the *Geographia*, c. 1415, Codex Vaticanus latinus 5689, Biblioteca Apostolica Vaticana, Rome, and in subsequent recensions. On d'Angelo see R. Weiss, "Iacopo Angeli da Scarperia (c. 1360-1410/ 11)," in *Medioevo e Renascimenta: Studi in Onore di Bruni Nardi* (Florence, 1955), 803-27.

2. There is no overall study of Jesuit cartography but a number of descriptions of their mapping of individual regions are scattered in the literature. Most fully described are the maps of China and Japan: see, for example, Joseph Needham and Wang Ling, *Science and Civilisation in China*, vol. 3, *Mathematics and the Sciences of the Heavens and the Earth* (Cambridge: Cambridge University Press, 1959), 583-86; H. Wallis, "The influence of Father Ricci on Far Eastern Cartography," *Imago Mundi* 19 (1965): 38-45; Theodore N. Foss, "A Western Interpretation of China: Jesuit Cartography," in *East Meets West: The Jesuits in China, 1552-1733*, ed. Charles E. Ronan and Bonnie B. L. Oh (Chicago: Loyola University Press, 1988), 209-51; *China Cartographica. Chinesische Kartenschätze und Europäische Forschungsdokumente.* (Berlin, 1983), 33-57; J. F. Schütte, "Maps of Japan by Father Girolamo de Angelis," *Imago Mundi* 9 (1952): 73-78; J. F. Schütte, "Ignacio Moreira of Lisbon, cartographer in Japan, 1590-92," *Imago Mundi* 16 (1962): 116-128. On Canada, see Conrad E. Heidenreich, "Mapping the Great Lakes, The Period of Exploration, 1603-1700," *Cartographica* 17, 3 (1980): 32-64; on Mexico, E. J. Burrus, *La Obra Cartographica de la provincia mexicana de la compania de Jesu (1567-1967)* (Madrid: 1967); on South America, "Maps of the Jesuit Mission in Spanish America, 18th century," *Imago Mundi* 15 (1960): 114-118, and G. Furland-Cardiff, *Cartografia jesuitica del Rio del la Plata* (Buenos Aires: 1936).

3. See François de Dainville, S.J., *La Géographie des humanistes* (Paris: Beauchesne, 1940); and François de Dainville, *L'Education de Jésuits (XVie-XVIIIE siècles)*, comp. Marie-Madeleine Compère, (Paris: Editions de Minuit, 1978).

4. Jonathan D. Spence, *The Memory Palace of Matteo Ricci* (London: Penguin, 1985), 145.

5. N. M. Crouse, *Contributions of the Canadian Jesuits to the Geographical Knowledge of New France: 1832-75* (Ithaca: Cornell University Press, 1924); Heidenreich, "Mapping the Great Lakes," 1980.

6. On Marquette as a cartographer see, for example, J. Delanglez, "Marquette's Autograph Map of the Mississippi River," *Mid-America* 27 (1945): 30-53.

7. Wallis, "The Influence of Father Ricci," 1965.

8. Pasquale M. d'Elia, *Recent Discoveries and New Studies (1938-1960) on the World Map in Chinese of Father Matteo Ricci, S.J.*, *Monumenta Serica* 20 (1961): 161.

9. Cordell D. K. Yee, "Traditional Chinese Cartography and the Myth of Westernization," in *The History of Cartography*, vol. 2, book 2, *Cartography in the Traditional East and Southeast Asian Societies*, ed. J. B. Harley and David Woodward (Chicago: The University of Chicago Press, forthcoming).

10. For the beginnings of this process see Donald F. Lach, *China in the Eyes of Europe: The Sixteenth Century* (Chicago: The University of Chicago Press, 1968), 816-21.

11. Jacques Gernet, *China and the Christian Impact: A Conflict of Cultures*, trans. Janet Lloyd (Cambridge: Cambridge University Press, 1985), 15.

12. Spence, *Memory Palace*, 96-97.

13. Spence, *Memory Palace*, 140.

14. See above, Jane ten Brink Goldsmith, "Jesuit Iconography."

15. Francesco Bressani, *Novae Franciae Accurata Delineatio*, 1657. Father Bressani was an Italian Jesuit who lived among the Huron from 1645 to 1649 before being forced to flee the Iroquois destruction. The map is reproduced in *The Mapping of the Great Lakes in the Seventeenth Century*. Twenty-two maps from the George S. and Nancy B. Parker Collection. A portfolio with an Introduction and Commentary by Kevin Kaufman (Providence, Rhode Island: The John Carter Brown Library, 1989).

Catalogue

Paintings

LEONAERT BRAMER
1596—Delft—1674

Leonaert Bramer began his career in Italy, where he learned the Italian fresco technique and enjoyed the distinguished patronage of Vincenzo Giustiniani and Don Camillo Pamphilli. He returned to his native town of Delft in 1628 with knowledge of the latest trends in Italian art. During the 1630s and 1640s Bramer produced small easel paintings, dealing primarily with religious subject matter. In the 1650s and 1660s he concentrated on large-scale decorative commissions in the town of Delft.

1. *The Glorification of Christianity,* c. 1635-37
    Oil on panel
    42 × 36 3/4 in. (106,7 × 93,3 cm)

Provenance: Purchased from Central Picture Galleries prior to 1962; Walter P. Chrysler Collections until 1989; on loan to the Chrysler Museum, Norfolk, Virginia, 1973-1989.

Literature: *Dutch Little Masters: Paintings by Seventeenth-Century Artists of the Netherlands,* lent by Walter P. Chrysler, Jr., An Exhibition of the Artmobile from The Arkansas Arts Center, 1962, p. 6.

Exhibitions: "A Focus on Recent Gifts," The Patrick & Beatrice Haggerty Museum of Art, Oct.-Nov., 1990.

Leonaert Bramer's *Glorification of Christianity* is unusual within the context of Dutch seventeenth century art. The painting includes "The Coronation of the Virgin" in the background and the four Latin Fathers of the Church in the foreground, while a vast array of Old and New Testament figures and early and later saints populate the rest of the painting.

The iconography of the painting is connected with Jesuit imagery in the sixteenth and seventeenth centuries. The *Glorification of Christianity* is related to Francesco Bassano's *Paradisio,* painted for the Gesù, in Rome. As Bassano, Bramer depicts the entire religious community. In the upper part of Bramer's painting "The Coronation of the Virgin" takes place with a youthful Christ present. During the Counter-Reformation, Catholic artists were urged to glorify the mother of God in defiance of Protestant reformers, and the Jesuits looked upon the Virgin as patroness and joint author of their order. The coronation of the Virgin was included in Rubens' picture cycle for the Jesuit church in Antwerp (1622). The four Latin church fathers seated in the foreground of Bramer's painting appeared on the drum of the cupola in the Gesù, in Rome and were also included by Rubens in his picture cycle.

While Calvinism was the official state religion in the Netherlands, Catholicism still managed to survive in the seventeenth century. By the second-half of the seventeenth century, there were over sixty clandestine Jesuit chapels in Amsterdam alone. Bramer's painting, which in size and proportions conforms to the format of altarpieces, is likely to have been produced for one of these clandestine places for Catholic worship.[J.t.B.G.]

Patrick and Beatrice Haggerty Museum of Art, Marquette University, Museum Purchase, with Cava Ross Estate Bequest (89.3)

GIUSEPPE CASTIGLIONE, S.J. (Chinese name, Lang Shih-ning)
Milan 1688—Peking 1768

Giuseppe Castiglione was an Italian Jesuit missionary, who was trained as a painter under Andrea Pozzo. Before leaving for China in 1714, he did several large altarpieces in Italy and Portugal. Castiglione landed in Macao in 1715, where he began to study the Chinese language and etiquette before presentation to Emperor K'ang Hsi in Beijing.

2. *Missionary Teaching of the Chinese*
   Ink and color on silk
   37 × 13 1/4 in. (94 × 33,7 cm)

Provenance: For 200 years in the Tintsin Family; Mrs. Victor di Suevero until 1942.

This painting was completed by Castiglione during his stay at the Chinese court. It dates from the Lien Lung period (1736-1795). The Chinese inscription that appears on the upper-right side of the painting was added at a later date: "This painting has no artist's signature. According to its style and brushwork, it must be done by Giuseppe Castiglione. It is one of his best works." This inscription is signed Yimou Song Xiaolian.

The artist's style is a curious mixture of Chinese and European art traditions. The silk picture support and the use of ink reflect Chinese painting technique; while the use of highly saturated colors in the costumes of the figures reflect European practice. Castiglione's treatment of the landscape, which is rendered in delicate and precise calligraphy, conforms entirely to Chinese art. The adoption of the vertical picture format is Chinese and runs counter to the European habit of employing a horizontal format for landscape paintings. The use of the vertical format also conforms to the decorative and non-illusionistic treatment of space that is typical of Chinese art. The facial physiognomies are a mixture of Chinese and western characteristics, treated, however, in a Chinese calligraphic mode. The costumes of the figures are more European than Chinese in appearance, with some fantasy elements included to give an "exotic" Chinese touch. The use of shading in the drapery to give a three-dimensional effect conforms to European, and not Chinese, practice.

Despite the overall Chinese appearance of the painting, its subject matter is typically Jesuit. A Jesuit missionary points to the heavens, alluded to with the sun, while an old man looks at him intently. The missionary has not yet caught the attention of the younger man in the foreground. The subject of this painting, focusing as it does on the Jesuit missionary effort, is typical of Jesuit iconography in the late-seventeenth and early-eighteenth century. [J.t.B.G.]

De Saisset Museum, Santa Clara University, Gift of Mrs. Victor di Suevero (1.227)

2. *Missionary Teaching of the Chinese*, 1688-1768
   Giuseppe Castiglione, S.J.

SEBASTIANO CONCA
1680—Gaeta—1764

A pupil of Francesco Solimena in Naples, Sebastiano Conca established himself in Rome in 1707. He obtained immense success in that city, drawing commissions from both Clement XI and Benedict XII. He was elected to the presidency of the Academy of St. Luke from 1729 until 1732, and again in 1739-1740. By courtesy of the Duke of Parma he established his studio in the apartments of the Palazzo Farnese. Conca spent the last twelve years of his life in Naples and Gaeta.

3. *Five Jesuit Martyrs of Cuncolim*
   Oil on canvas
   38 × 49 in. (97,5 × 125 cm)

Literature: *Museo de Arte de Ponce,* Catalogue of Paintings and Sculpture of the European and American Schools (Julius Held, Rene Taylor, James N. Carder), (Ponce, Puerto Rico: 1984); Catalogue I, 109f, attr. Carlo Maratti; Erich Schleier, "La Pittura italiana del sei e settecento nel Museo di Ponce: nuove proposte e problemi attributivi, *Antichità viva,* fasc. I, (1980) 24, pl. 7.

Exhibitions: Museo de la Universidad de Puerto Rico, "17 Pinturas de Grandes Maestros," Jan.-Feb. 1960, no. 4.

The five youthful Jesuits were martyred on July 25, 1583 at Cuncolim in the district of Salcete, Goa, India. Though the process had begun as far back as 1600, they were not finally canonized until 1741. Father Rudolph Acquaviva (born 1550), son of the duke of Atri, cousin of St. Aloysius Gonzaga and nephew of Claudio Acquaviva, who had become general of the Society of Jesus, was cut by a scimitar and spear. Father Alphonsus Pacheco (born *c.* 1551) suffered death by mutilation; Father Anthony Francis (born 1553) was pierced by arrows and had his head split open with a sword; Brother Francis Arantha (born *c.* 1551) received blows from a scimitar and a lance, but was killed by arrows. Comparison of the five figures with the rendering of the five martyrs on the frontispiece of the *Vita Beati P. Ignatii Loiolae* (Rome, 1609) reveals that the central figure is Father Acquaviva, socially the most prominent among the group. The presence of haloes around the heads of the figures may mean that the painting was done in or after 1741, perhaps specifically to celebrate their canonization.

This painting was previously attributed to Carlo Maratti. Federico Zeri has suggested an attribution to Francesco Mancini (1694-1758). The attribution to Conca is owed to Erich Schleier. It would thus represent a rare instance of Jesuit iconography in the artist's *oeuvre.* Stylistically, it can be related to the *St. Benedict Giving the Rules of his Order to St. Mauro and St. Placido* (formerly Milan, Finarte 1973), which can be dated in the 1740s and to *St. Juan of Sahagun* of 1750, in the Convent of the Salesians in Orihuela (Alicante). [J.t.B.G./J.P.M.]

Museo de Arte, Ponce, Puerto Rico, The Luis A. Ferré Foundation (58.0067)

GIUSEPPE MARIA CRESPI
1665—Bologna—1747

Crespi studied with Carlo Cignani and Domenico Maria Canuti, two exponents of the Baroque style in Bologna, but more important for the development of Crespi's art were the influence of the Venetian school—of Paolo Veronese in particular—and of his great Bolognese predecessors, Ludovico Carraci, Guercino and Cavedone, Crespi began his career as a fresco painter but turned rapidly to easel painting. He executed many altarpieces for churches in Emilia and acquired greater fame yet for his genre scenes. These won him the patronage of wealthy individuals as well as of sovereigns, Ferdinando de Medici and the Elector of Palatinate, for instance.

4.   *A Jesuit Mission,* c. 1710
     Oil on canvas
     20 7/8 × 25 in. (63 × 52,5 cm)

Provenance: Marchese Zacchia Rondanini, Bologna; Carlo Foresti, Milan; Jacob Heimann, Milan; Given by him to the Detroit Institute of Arts.

Literature: Francesco Malaguzzi Valeri, "Palazzi e Ville Bolognese; il Palazzo Zacchia Rondanini Reggiani," *Cronache d'Arte,* V May-June 1928, p. 215; P.T. Rathbone, "The Jesuit Mission by Giuseppe Maria Crespi," *DIA Bulletin,* XVIII, no. 4 (Jan. 1939) 4-6, reprod.

Exhibitions: *Three Baroque Masters: Strozzi, Crespi, Piazzetta,* Baltimore Museum of Art, Baltimore, Maryland, 1944, p. 31, no. 20, reprod.; *Giuseppe Maria Crespi,* (M. Merriman, Milan, 1980). p. 315, no. 276, reprod.

Crespi's genre scenes were immensely popular during the artist's own lifetime. While many of them are little more than fanciful depictions of popular subjects, others—such as this one—carry a barely hidden moral message. On one hand this depiction of a Jesuit priest preaching in the midst of an outdoor gathering belongs to the kind of representation of fair scenes for which Crespi had earned fame (his *Fair at Poggio a Caiano,* 1709, had won him the patronage of the Florentine court), but on the other hand it betrays a more profound concern on the part of the artist; Crespi was a devout painter who, throughout his life, worked on important commissions for the Church. Whether the product of his own imagination or of a commission, this work makes a direct comment on the role and importance of Jesuits in contemporary society. While their "mission" was associated primarily with the evangelization of far-away countries, their role and presence on the more familiar terrain of Italy were equally important. Preachers and confessors reminded their parishioners of their religious duties with a zeal equal to the one they brought to converting non-Christians.

In this picture the Jesuit is represented addressing a group of people, some of whom are carefully listening while others are engaged in such activities as gambling. Whatever the original destination of the painting (it may have been painted for a prominent Venetian family), its moral message should not be underestimated. [J.P.M.]

The Detroit Institute of Arts, Gift of Jacob Heilmann (38.88)

LUDOVICO MAZZANTI
Orvieto 1679—Viterbo 1775

Mazzanti was a student of Giovanni Battista Gaulli, whose ceiling painting depicting *The Adoration of the Name of Jesus* for the Gesù is one of the most important contributions of Jesuit art. Mazzanti was also influenced by the Italian painter, Luca Giordano. He became a member of the Academy of St. Luke in Rome in 1744. Mazzanti did many religious paintings for Jesuit churches. Among his most important works in this category are an altarpiece for S. Andrea al Quirinale, a ceiling painting in S. Ignatius, and an altarpiece in S. Apollinare.

5.   *The Death of St. Francis Xavier*
     Oil on canvas
     18 × 13 7/8 in.

St. Francis Xavier, the greatest missionary during the pioneer period of the Jesuits, set sail for India in April, 1541. He left India in April 1552 and in September entered the Bay of Canton, landing on the desolate island of Sancian. The island was as hideout for Chinese smugglers and was used by Portuguese traders as well. Determined to get to China, Francis tried to entice some smugglers to take him there, but none wanted to take the risk. He eventually hired one of them to transport him to the mainland. But after he had paid him, the man disappeared. Then suddenly on November 21 of that year he took ill and was confined to his leafy hut on the shore of the island. His Christian Chinese servant, Antonio, faithfully cared for him in his final illness and years later wrote an account of the saint's last days. On November 28, Francis went into a coma, but regained consciousnes in December. Throughout his waking hours he prayed constantly, until the morning of December 3, when he died. His body was buried on the island, and when spring came his remains were taken to Malacca, and a few years after that to Goa where they were interred in the church Bom Jesus.

This painting combines the death of St. Francis Xavier with a visionary ecstasy. Placed prominently in the foreground, the saint holds a small crucifix. His face, suggesting a state of semi-consciousness, is turned upwards, as he gazes at a host of cherubs who emerge from the clouds in a surge of dazzling light. The saint is accompanied by a Jesuit companion, who bends over him with religious fervor, and his Chinese servant, who looks upon him with deep reverence. This event takes place in a landscape setting executed in a typically Venetian style. Three turbaned figures gesture towards the saint from the distance; beyond is a harbor, alluding to his life as as missionary.

The painting may be a preparatory sketch for a painting by Mazzanti in the Haute Collection in Düsseldorf (*Versteigerungskatalog* 387, Lempertz, Koln, Cat. no. 31, plate 24). The Düsseldorf painting is signed with the monogram L M. [J.t.B.G.]

Philadelphia Museum of Art, Bloomfield Moore Collection (83-89)

6. *St. Louis Gonzaga in Glory,* 1696-1782
Attributed to Francesco De Mura

Attributed to **FRANCESCO DE MURA**
1696—Naples—1782

6. *St. Louis Gonzaga in Glory*
    Oil on canvas
    59 1/2 × 39 1/2 in. (151 × 101 cm)

St. Louis Gonzaga (1568-1591), also known as St. Aloysius Gonzaga, was the eldest son of a Spanish marquis. At the age of seven, Louis converted from a courtly to a more interior life. He began to pray and enjoyed reciting the Psalms. At the age of nine, he was taken to Florence to learn the customs of princely life at the Medici court. Finding court life repulsive, Louis continued to find comfort in a spiritual existence. He returned to Spain in 1582, at the age of fourteen and on August 15, 1583, while praying before an image of Our Lady in a Jesuit church, he let it be known to the confessor that he wished to join the Order. Encountering opposition from his father, Louis did not take the Jesuit vows until November 25, 1587, two years after he entered the novitiate of S. Andrea al Quirinale in Rome.

The scene depicted in the painting takes place in a heavenly setting composed of dense clouds and radiant light. St. Louis Gonzaga is seated beneath the Virgin with the young Christ on her lap. The book St. Louis Gonzaga holds in his right hand probably the constitution of the Jesuit Order. The red dress of Mary refers to the Passion of Christ, the blue drapery, to her heavenly nature. The blue and gold of Louis garment refer to the Jesuit order. The saint is accompanied here by a group of young Jesuit novices; angels and putti gaze down from the heavens.

Glories of saints were popular in Counter-Reformation imagery. In this particular instance, however, the scene is given added relevance, referring as it does to the moment when Louis prayed before an image of the Virgin in a Jesuit church in Spain. This was the moment of his conversion. Moreover, the representation of Louis actually experiencing the presence of the Virgin conforms to the type of religious experience described by Ignatius in *The Spiritual Exercises*. This painting also confirms the Jesuit notion that pictures can help the young novice experience events and the lives of religious personages.

The painting is executed in a style anchored in Bolognese classicism of the late-sixteenth and early-seventeenth century. This style is primarily associated with the Annibale and Ludovico Carracci, however, the painting is more closely related to the works of the Italian artist, Giovanni Lanfranco, himself influenced by Bolognese classicism. [J.t.B.G.]

The Art Museum, Princeton University, Gift of J. McCrindle (1979-8)

ACISCLO ANTONIO PALOMINO Y VELASCO
Bujalance (Córdoba) 1655—1726 Madrid

Palomino was the most important fresco painter in seventeenth-century Spain. His most well-known works are his frescoes for churches in Madrid, Salamanca, and Granada. In 1688 he was appointed painter to the king. He was also a scholar who wrote about art. The first volume of his *Museo Pictóhrico y Escale Optica* was published in 1715; the second volume in 1724. The second volume included a third part entitled *Parnaso Español Laureado*, a collection of biographies of Spanish painters, which is an important source for the history of Spanish painting from the fifteenth to the seventeenth centuries.

7. *Saint Francis Borgia Kneeling Before the Body of Queen Isabella of Spain Before Joining the Jesuit Order*
    42 × 49 1/4 in. (106,7 × 125,1 cm)

Signed lower-right: Ant. Palomino P. Regis (kings painter after 1688)

Provenance: Possibly done for the chapel of the Ducal family Osuna, Valencia, c. 1695 (St. Francis Borgia was a member of the Osuna family).

During the seventeenth-century religious scenes and portraits were the favored subjects of Spanish artists. This painting, attributed by Dr. Priscilla Muller to the court painter and art theorist, Palomino, combines portraiture with religious subject matter. The subject of the painting is the conversion of Francis Borgia (1510-1572), a Spanish nobleman, to the monastic life.

Born into a nobel family and educated in the humanities and music, Francis was only twenty years old when in 1530 he was made Marquis of Lombay and placed in charge of the imperial household. He was much beloved by Queen Isabella, whose unexpected death in 1539 made a lasting impression upon him. It was this incident that caused Francis to reflect upon the tragic transitoriness of human life and material possession which resulted in his conversion.

The saint is depicted as a young nobleman kneeling before the remains of Queen Isabella; behind him several figures recoil at the gruesome sight. The scene depicted did not actually occur, but serves as a moral allegory. The young Francis holds a piece of cloth draped about the crowned skeletal remains of Queen Isabella. The skeletal figure is a "*momento mori,*" alluding to the transitoriness of temporal power. A strip of paper next to the saint contains the inscription: "Nuca mas Servir a Senor q'seme pueda morir" (never again will I serve a man who can rot/die).

Skulls were often depicted in the seventeenth century in Dutch still-life paintings as an allusion to the transient nature of the material world. Here the popular motif is invoked with specific religious reference. The three Cardinals' hats on the floor beside Borgia represent his choice of a religious life over that of service to the temporal kingdom, and an angel above points to the "IHS" monograph, the emblem of the Jesuit order.

St. Francis became the Society's third Father General, and it was during his term of office that the first Jesuit missionaries came to Florida. These were the earliest Jesuit missions on American soil. He was beatified by Urban VIII in 1624 and canonized by Clement X in 1671. This manner of portraying him is entirely unique. [J.t.B.G.]

Anonymous Private Collection

8. *Brazilian Landscape,* 1612-1680
Frans Post

9. *Design for a Chapelin Vienna*, 1642-1709
Andrea Pozzo

FRANS POST
Leiden *c.* 1612—Haarlem 1680

Frans Post belonged to a retinue of artists, architects, engineers, explorers, scientists, and poets who accompanied Johan Maurits, Count of Nassau-Siegen to the Dutch colony of Pernambuco, in Brazil, in 1637. Returning with Maurits and his retinue to the Netherlands in 1644, Post specialized in the production of landscape paintings representing Brazil. These landscapes, long admired for their charming description of exotic plants and animals, can be tied to the scientific interests of the count, whose palaces in Pernambuco included vast botanical gardens and a *Tiergarten* with all the known species of animals inhabiting the Brazilian terrain.

8. *Brazilian Landscape,* 1665
    Oil and canvas
    22 × 32 3/4 in. (55,9 × 83,2 cm)

Signed and dated lower left: F. Post, 1665

Provenance: Dr. Siegfried F. Aram, New York, 1934.

Literature: R. C. Smith, "The Brazilian Landscapes of Frans Post," *The Art Quarterly,* vol. 1, no. 4 (1938) 238-267, fig. 15 (as "Visit to a Ruined Chapel"); J. de Sousa-Leao, *Frans Post* (New York: Abner Schram Publishers, 1973) no. 48, 88-89, (as "Church with Portico").

Exhibitions: Montreal Museum of Fine Arts, Quebec, *The Painter and the New World,* June 8-July 30, 1967, no. 9;, Jane Vorhees Zimmerli Art Museum, Rutgers, The State University of New Jersey, *Haarlem: The Seventeenth Century,* Feb. 20-April 17, 1983, no. 100 (ill.); *The Age of the Marvelous,* 1991-1993, Hannover/Raleigh, N.C./Houston/Atlanta).

Completed late in Post's career, this painting depicts figures entering a Jesuit church in a lush and exotic landscape setting [for the identification of the church in this painting as a Jesuit church, see Robert C. Smith, Jr., "The Brazilian Landscapes of Frans Post," *The Art Quarterly* I (1938), p. 257. The author is tempted to connect this painting with one given by the Count of Nassau to Louis XIV, which is described in the following way: "This is the ruins of the fine church of the Jesuit fathers in the town of Olinda, which was richly adorned with gold inside; they still say the mass there and perform their worship. . ."]. The church, which is in a somewhat ruined state, is built in the severe Portuguese Renaissance style with a classical portico. Elegantly attired figures entering the church are accompanied by black servants. In the landscape setting one can recognize *dendezeiro* palms, *juá* trees, tropical fruit trees and flowering vines. An armadillo, a monkey, a cobra killing a hare, and numerous reptiles populate the landscape foreground.

While cartographers of the period celebrated Dutch colonialism in mapping the New World, Post's topography portrays a world without reference to the Dutch commercial presence in Brazil. The Portuguese architecture of the church refers to the Portuguese and Jesuit presence prior to the arrival of the Dutch in Pernambuco. Nature is conceived here as a pastoral world unencumbered by Dutch mercantilism and urbanism. While the cobra killing the hare may be a reference to political realities, plants and animals dominate the landscape in a spirit of peaceful coexistence. Seen in this context, the Jesuit church may be understood as a metaphor for the golden, peaceful past conjured up in Post's exotic landscape.[J.t.B.G.]

The Detroit Institute of Arts, Founders' Society Purchase, Membership and Donations Fund (34.188)

ANDREA POZZO
Trent 1642—Vienna 1709

Best known as a master of illusionistic ceiling decoration, Pozzo was also an architect and a writer on art. He is one of the few Jesuit painters to achieve special distinction in seventeenth-century art. He entered the Jesuit school in Trent at the age of seventeen, but soon left to study painting. In 1665 he entered the cloisters in Milan as a Jesuit. During his first decade in the noviate he was active as a painter in Milan. At the end of 1681 he was called to Rome by General Oliva at the recommendation of the Roman painter, Carlo Maratta. Once in Rome, Pozzo received many commissions to provide painted decorations for Jesuit churches. His most important work in Rome is his ceiling painting in S. Ignazio, which depicts an *Allegory of the Missionary Work of the Jesuits* (1691-94).

9. *Design for a Chapel in Vienna*, c. 1705
   Oil on canvas
   29 1/8 × 24 1/8 in. (74 × 61,3 cm)

Literature: *The Art Quarterly* XXIV, 1961, 100, reprod. p. 96; Bernard Kerber, *Andrea Pozzo.* (Berlin and New York: 1971) 88-89, plate 68.

In 1702, Father Andrea Pozzo left Rome for Vienna, where he had been called by Emperor Leopold (in 1693 and 1700, Pozzo had dedicated the volumes of his treatise on perspective to him). During the brief years he spent in Vienna until his death, Pozzo produced a considerable body of work. Among his main commissions were frescoes (no longer preserved) for the Favorita (now Theresianum), the remodeling of the Church of the Jesuit University, frescoes and projects for altars in many Viennese churches such as the Peterskirche and the Annaskirche, not to mention large decorations for the "Gartenpalast" of the Lichtenstein family, an important patron who had also been keen on Pozzo's move to Austria.

It has not yet been possible to establish for which church this *modello* was intended. Commenting on the work, Kerber seems to exclude the possibility of it being a mere fantasy on the part of the artist, and remarks that the representation of St. Thomas of Villanova on the left cartouche may imply that the *modello* was in fact intended for the church of the Augustinians. For Kerber, this type of *modello* was meant to clarify the linear ideas, Pozzo would have presented in a drawing. In particular, it indicates the prominent part the light falling from the upper windows—casting shadows or being picked up by the brightly gilded decorations and sculptures—would play in order to enhance the emotional impact to the ensemble. [J.P.M.]

The University of Michigan Museum of Art, Ann Arbor (1960/2.124)

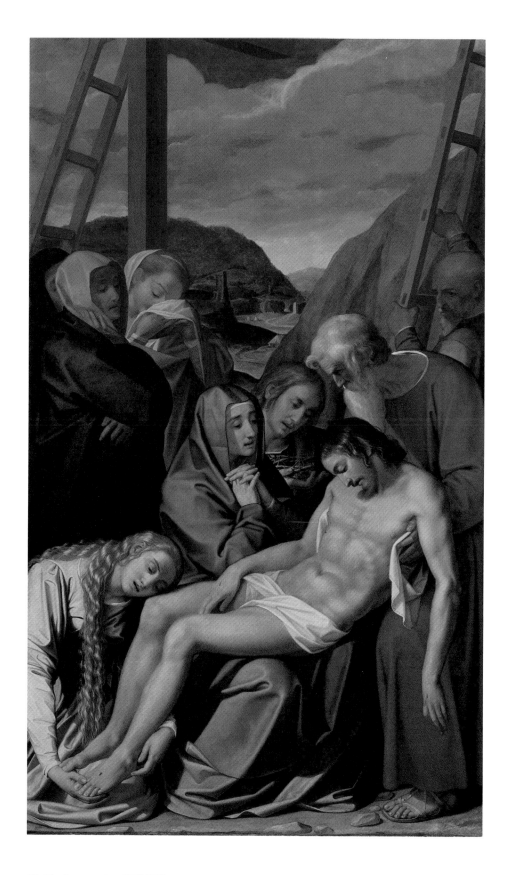

10. *The Lamentation,* 1569-1598
   Scipione Pulzone

SCIPIONE PULZONE
Active Rome between 1569—1598

Pulzone first began his career as a portrait painter, a genre in which, according to his biographer Giovanni Baglione, he excelled. Later in life, he shifted to the painting of religious compositions with the same clarity and forthrightness that had characterized his portraits. This put him somewhat in opposition to the exponents of the late Mannerist style, such as Federico Zuccaro, but won him instead the patronage of the new religious orders of the Counter-Reformation in Rome. He worked for the Oratorians at Santa Maria in Vallicella, and was commissioned works for three chapels in the Church of the Gesù.

10. *The Lamentation*
     Oil on canvas
     114 × 68 in. (290 × 127 cm)

Signed and dated: Scipio Caiet(a)/nus Faci(e)bat An(n)o Dni/Md.Cxi

Literature: F. Zeri, *Pittura e Controriforma: L'arte senza tempo di Scipione da Gaeta*, Turin, 1957 p. 68 ff., 73,79,82 ff.,111,n.47,figs.90,91; H. Hibbard, "Ut picturae sermones: The First Painted Decorations of the Gesù" in *Baroque Art: The Jesuit Contribution.* (New York: 1972) 38,44 fig.27; The Metropolitan Museum of Art, Notable acquisitions 1983-1984, selected by Phillippe de Montebello, Director, 62-63; Erasmo Vaudo, *Scipione Pulzone da Gaetta, Pittore,* 1976, p. 37, note 26, plate 39.

This important and majestic altarpiece was commissioned from the artist to be placed in the third chapel to the right in the Church of the Gesù. The altarpiece is dated 1591, and the chapel for which it was intended was consecrated in 1593. The Jesuit architect and painter Giuseppe Valeriano who, like Pulzone, participated directly in the decoration of the church, and also in the planning of its program, was responsible for the selection of the artist, whom he had previously employed in the decoration of other chapels in the same church. The altarpiece had a great impact on the public, its importance and quality being immediately noted by critics such as Guiseppe Baglione. Much admired for over a century, it was removed during later remodeling for the church to be replaced by a painting of St. Francis Borgia by Andrea Pozza. Since so much of the present decoration of the Gesù has replaced the original one, earlier documents of the church's original appearance, such as this altarpiece strongly marked by the spirit of the Counter-Reformation, are particularly important. [J.P.M.]

The Metropolitan Museum of Art, New York, Purchase, Anonymous Gift in Memory of Terence Cardinal Cooke (1984.74)

Sculpture

ROMAN, 17TH CENTURY

11. *Saint Ignatius Loyola and His Companions and Followers*
     Bronze
     11 1/2 × 10 7/8 in. (29,2 × 27,4 cm)

Literature: John Goldsmith Phillips, "Renaissance Bronzes, a New Installation and Recent Acquisitions," in *Bulletin of the Metropolitan Museum of Art,* vol. XXXV, Number 6, June 1940, 127-129, fig. 2.

One of the major and holiest features of the Church of the Gesù in Rome is the Ignatius altar. The complete altar was designed by Andrea Pozzo, and is flanked by vigorous sculptures by Pierre II Le Gros. The lower part of the altar itself is a large urn made of gilded bronze which represents Saint Ignatius and his followers. The urn in bronze has been attributed in the past to Alessandro Algardi, but the attribution has been challenged and could not apply to this bronze—a 17th century replica of the original urn in any case. The relief represents Saint Ignatius holding the Constitution of the Society of Jesus. He is surrounded by Saint Francis Xavier, St. Francis Borgia, St. Aloysius Gonzaga and the Polish saint, Stanislas Kostka. Other figures include St. Robert Bellamine, St. Peter Canisius, a participant in the Council of Trent who authored a catechism, Ignatius Azevedo showing a follower a copy of the icon of the Virgin Mary in Santa Maria Maggiore that he had taken along on his mission to South America. There are also three Japanese saints, John de Goto, Paul Miki and James Kisai, showing the instruments of their martyrdom, and Andrew de Ovidio, bishop of Ethiopia.

The origin of this bronze replica is not known. It was certainly intended to decorate a Jesuit church or the chapel of a personality particularly close to the order.[J.P.M.]

The Metropolitan Museum of Art, The Rogers Fund (38.152.20)

11. *Saint Ignatius Loyola and His Companions and Followers*, 1595-1654
    Roman, 17th Century

12. **NORTH ITALIAN (MILAN),** 18th Century
St. Francis Borgia
Bronze
Height including base, 43 3/5 (111 cm)

The prototype for this bronze was designed by Ciro Ferri (1634-1689) for the Church of the Gesù in Rome. It is one of a little known series of eight figures for which Ferri was responsible. Divided into two groups of four, eight Jesuit saints were placed on the altars of Ignatius Loyola and Francis Xavier. St. Francis Xavier, St. Theresa, St. Philip Neri, and St. Isidro Agricola, were placed on the altar of Ignatius Loyola; St. Francis Borgia, St. Francis of Sales, St. Francis Paola and St. Francis of Assisi decorated the altar of St. Francis Xavier of the Sacristy.

St. Francis Borgia, canonized in 1671, is considered to be the second founder of the Jesuits. He is often depicted standing on an upturned crown, the symbol of his renounced nobility. This statue probably held a monstrance or a chalice.

The treatment of the figure is derived from seventeenth-century Italian examples of religious sculpture. The strong facial characterization of St. Francis Borgia, and the expressive treatment of the hands, as well as the combination of descriptive realism and dramatic force in the drapery may be connected with the work of religious sculpture of Bernini.

A number of provenances have been suggested for this work. Comparisons have been made to the work of Pierre Le Gros the Younger (1666-1719), a Frenchman who made his career in Rome. A Milanese provenance has also been posited. This work recalls the bronze portrait figures of the sculptors, Leone and Pompe Leoni, who both worked at the Spanish court. The bronzes they produced there were cast in Milan. However, published research is lacking in the activities of Milanese workshops after the deaths of the Leoni.[J.t.B.G.]

Courtesy of Valery Taylor Gallery, New York

Drawings

MARCO BENEFIAL
1684—Rome—1764

Relatively little is known about Marco Benefial. Between 1698 and 1703, he studied with a Bolognese painter, Bonaventura Lamberti. Apparently through him Benefial became aware of antique sculpture, of Raphael and of the Bolognese masters. Benefial's eclectic inspiration may account for the pleasing style that insured him many commissions. In spite of his success, Benefial was not fully adopted by the Roman art establishment. He becamed a member of the Academia di San Luca only in 1746. Nine years later he was expelled from the institution because of his frequent criticisms of fellow academicians.

13. *Study for a Group Portrait,* c. 1756
    Brush gray wash with traces of black chalk on cream laid paper
    9 1/8 × 12 5/8 in. (23,2 × 32 cm)

Provenance: Leo S. Olschski, Florence (1965).

Literature: *One Hundred Items from the Stock of Leo S. Olschski Bookseller,* cat. 142, Florence, 1965, p. 59, no. 80, repr.; Anthony M. Clark: "Manners and Methods of Benefial," *Paragone,* vol. 17, no. 199 (September 1966), p. 26, pl. 21; Mario Praz, Conversation Pieces: A Survey of the Informal Group Portrait in Europe and America, University Park, Pa, 1971, p. 202, no. 9; *A Scholar Collects,* Selections from the Anthony Morris Clark Bequest, Philadelphia Museum of Art, 1980-1981, 41-42, no. 29, reprod.

This drawing relates directly to a painting by the artist, dated 1756, in the Galleria Nazionale d'Arte Antica, Rome, representing the Marefoschi family. The drawing, is however, a straightforward rendition of a subject common in Baroque and Rococo iconography, St. Francis Xavier preaching. Given the rather frequent occurence of the subject and the fact that no details point out in that direction, it is difficult to subscribe to the late Anthony Clark's opinion that the drawing was a mock representation of a Jesuit scene. Rather it seems that the artist first executed this sketch and that, pleased with his composition he adapted it to the needs of the group portrait he was painting at the same time, whimsically keeping the Chinese costumes in his depiction of the Roman family who had commissioned the portrait. It was not particularly uncommon for painters to adopt particularly successful compositional schemes from religious to secular representations, or vice-versa.[J.P.M.]

Philadelphia Museum of Art, Bequest of Anthony M. Clark (1978-70-185)

GIUSEPPE BOTTANI
Cremona 1717—Mantua 1784

A native of Cremona, Bottani first studied with a Florentine artist Vincenzo Meucci. When he arrived in Rome in 1735, he studied with Agostino Masucci. Both teachers were instrumental in leading the younger artist in a direction that, with late Bolognese Academicism, was in strong reaction to the Baroque. The more advanced, but contemporary, attempts of artists such as Batoni or Mengs to incorporate a certain vision of the past in their own style, were for Bottani a further incentive to work in a manner that was modern without eschewing the lessons of the past. He was elected to the Accademia of S. Luca in 1758, also taught at the Accademia del Nudo, and had a successful career, providing many works for the Church as well as for wealthy clients, the Rospigliosi and Doria Pamphili families in particular. Bottani moved to Mantua in 1769 to assume the responsibilities of Director of the academy, where he played a seminal role.

14. *Studies of the Heads for "Saint Louis Gonzaga and Saint Stanislas Kostka Adoring the Madonna and Child,"* c. 1750-65
Black and white chalk on gray prepared paper
11 1/16 × 15 9/16 in. (28,1 × 39,7 cm)

Provenance: The artist's heirs, Rome; Angelo di Castro, Rome, 1969; Anthony M. Clark.

Literature: *A Scholar Collects*, Selections from the Anthony Morris Clark Bequest, Philadelphia Museum of Art, 1980-1981, p. 63, no. 50, reprod.

Exhibitions: The Minneapolis Institute of Arts, Minneapolis, Minnesota, "Eighteenth-Century Italian Paintings, Drawings, Sculpture, and Decorative Arts," Nov. 1970-Jan. 1971.

This drawing is the only known study for a painting representing the two Jesuit saints adoring the Madonna and Child in the chapel of the diocesan seminary at Pontremoli. The painting has traditionally been attributed to Giovanni Bottani, Guiseppe's younger brother and collaborator, but the quality of parts of the painting such as the heads of the saints has led critics to believe that it was at least a collaboration between the two artists. Stefano Susinno, commenting on this drawing (see *A Scholar Collects*, p. 63) has noted both the dependence of the work in Pontremoli upon the painting of the same subject executed in 1765, probably by Stefano Pozzi, for the first chapel on the right in the church of Sant'Ignazio, Rome, and the rarity of the subject. Sussino writes that the subject "bears witness to a renewed interest in the Society of Jesus, especially in connection with youth and with educational institutions, just at the time in which anti-Jesuit polemics, which were to result in the suppression of the society in 1773, were at their height.[J.P.M.]

Philadelphia Museum of Art, Bequest of Anthony M. Clark (1978-70-200)

GIUSEPPE CADES
1750—Rome—1799

Giuseppe Cades was both painter and etcher. He was admitted to the Academy of St. Luke in Rome in 1766. Patronized by the Chigi family, he provided painted decorations for their country villa in Ariccia with scenes from the pastoral tale of Armida and Daifilo. His style is based on the study of the great masters of Italian Renaissance painting. His drawings, in particular, show the influence of Raphael.

15. *St. Francis Xavier Embarking for India*, c. 1790
     Pen and brown ink and brown washes, over faint traces of black chalk on cream laid paper
     5 1/8 × 3 1/4 in. (13,2 × 8,4 cm)

Provenance: Collection of Helene Seiferheld.

Exhibitions: Minneapolis, Minnesota, The Minneapolis Institute of Arts, "Roman Eighteenth-Century Drawings form a Private Collection," February 11—March 19, 1967, no. 17; "Eighteenth-Century Italian Paintings, Drawings, Sculpture, and Decorative Arts:; Nov. 24, 1970—January 10, 1971 (no catalogue); Philadelphia, Pennsylvania, "A Scholar Collects, Selections from the Anthony Morris Clark Bequest," October 2, 1980—January 4, 1981, no. 71.

St. Francis Xavier was the most important missionary during the pioneer age of the Jesuits. He came to know St. Ignatius Loyola during his early years of study, and was convinced to join the Jesuit cause. He responded to St. Ignatius' interest in the Holy Land by agreeing in 1534 to go there to convert infidels.

Unable to reach the Holy Land because of Venice's war with the Turks, Xavier was given approval by the Pope to go with a group of nine other Jesuits to the new Portuguese colony in India. As Xavier was boarding the *Santiago* in Lisbon, the king's messenger handed him a papal letter appointing him apostolic nuncio; this gave him authority over all Portuguese clergy in Goa, India. The ship sailed on April 7, 1541.

In this drawing Xavier is depicted with a group of Jesuits boarding the ship in Lisbon. A halo over Xavier head proclaims the saintly status that he achieved after his death. The Jesuit companion to his immediate left holds a book, alluding to the Jesuit mission to convert heathens to Christianity. While no messenger is shown handing Xavier a letter, this moment of his departure is symbolic, since it was then that he was appointed apostolic nuncio. Thus, the image is not simply narrative, but also alludes to the legitimization of the Jesuit enterprise by the papacy. The drawing may have been done as a preliminary design for a print or illustration.[J.t.B.G.]

Philadelphia Museum of Art, Bequest of Anthony M. Clark (1978-70-211)

CIRO FERRI
1634—Rome—1689

A pupil of Pietro da Cortona, with whom he collaborated and whose work he frequently copied, Ferri was patronized by Pope Alexander VI, the Borghese family, and Cosimo III de'Medici. Cosimo invited him to complete the frescoes left unfinished by Pietro da Cortona at the Palazzo Pitti. Ciro Ferri was also a sculptor and executed four statues for the sacristy of the Gesù.

16. *The Death of St. Francis Xavier*
    Black chalk on cream laid paper
    20 × 12 1/2 in. (51 × 32 cm)

Provenance: Purchased in Los Angeles, 1966.

Exhibitions: New York, The Metropolitan Museum of Art, "17th-Century Italian Drawings in the Metropolitan Museum of Art," 1979 (catalogue by Jacob Bean, no. 172).

The most celebrated seventeenth-century representation of the death of St. Francis Xavier is Carlo Maratti's painting (commissioned 1674, completed 1679) on the altar dedicated to that saint in the Gesù, in Rome. The architectural and sculptural elements of this altar were designed by Pietro da Cortona, but work on the altar was not begun until three years after his death. Cortona's early involvement with this enterprise makes it possible that his principal assistant, Ciro Ferri, may have hoped to obtain the commission for the painted altarpiece. Though Maratti's composition has a square top and Ferri's a rounded one, they have a number of figural elements in common, especially the pose of the dying saint in the foreground. It is unclear whether Ferri was influenced by Maratti or vice versa.

The illusionistic niche that frames the scene is the kind of arch employed in early Christian basilicas, and hence conjures up early church history. However, the scene depicted concerns the life a contemporary saint. Such analogies between Jesuit activities and the early Christian past are characteristic of Jesuit iconography.

Francis Xavier, the greatest missionary of the church, is depicted in a manner that recalls the lamentation of Christ. Mourning figures surround him and three cherubs flying next to palm branches above allude to martyrdom. While Francis Xavier did not die a martyr's death, the analogy with Christ celebrates his saintly status.[J.t.B.G.]

The Metropolitan Museum of Art, 1966, Purchase of 1966, Mrs. Carl. Shelden and Florence and Carl Shelden Foundation Gifts (66.9)

17. *The Ecstasy of Stanislas Kostka*, c. 1679
Black chalk and pencil on white laid paper, backed with Japanese paper
(18 1/2 × 13 in. (47,2 × 33 cm)

Provenance: H. Schickman Gallery, New York; purchased by the Allen Art Museum in 1974.

Literature: Oberlin, Allen Art Museum, Catalogue. . . ., no. 121.

The brief life of the Polish saint Stanislas Kostka (1550-1568) became a frequent subject in Jesuit iconography after the beatification of the young Polish aristocrat in 1670—and his subsequent canonization in 1726. Typically, this drawing depicts Stanislas Kostka in ecstasy, being comforted by angels. The representation draws from two stories associated with the saint's life: a vision of the Madonna he had while in Vienna (an event that prompted him to join the Society of Jesus), and his receiving the communion from a angel.

Ciro Ferri often worked for Jesuit patrons. This drawing was executed as a modello for an altarpiece in the Jesuit novitiate church of Sant'Andrea al Quirinale in Rome. Ferri's project was not realized, and while he executed another altarpiece for the same church, the commission for the one honoring Stanislas Kostka went to Carlo Maratta in 1679 (Maratta's altarpiece was completed in 1687). It is likely that Ciro Ferri's drawing was executed between the completion of the church in 1670 and 1679.[J.P.M.]

Allen Memorial Art Museum, Oberlin College, Friends of the Endowment Fund (74.56)

ANDREA POZZO

18.   *Study for the Altar of Saint Louis Gonzaga in Sant'Ignazio, Rome,* c. 1697
      Red chalk on cream laid paper
      10 3/4 × 8 9/16 in. (27,3 × 21,8 cm)

Provenance: Gift of Andrew S. Ciechanowiecki, London; Anthony M. Clark.

Literature: *A Scholar Collects,* Selections from the Anthony Morris Clark Bequest, Philadelphia Museum of Art, 1980-1981, 11-12, no. 2, reprod.

Exhibitions: Metropolitan Museum of Art, New York, *Roman Artists of the 17th Century: Drawings and Prints,* Nov. 2, 1976—Jan. 16, 1977.

The church of St. Ignatius in Rome is, with the Gesù, a manifesto of Jesuit art. It witnesses the brilliant contribution of Jesuit artists to the fields of architecture, painting and decoration in 17th century Rome. The first stone of St. Ignatius was laid in 1626, but the church was formally opened to the public in 1650. Even by then, most of its decoration was far from being completed. If a Jesuit architect, Horatio Grassi (1583-1654) was instrumental in designing the church, its final appearance is owed to the extraordinary contribution of the painter, decorator and theroretician Andrea Pozzo. Pozzo's particular interest was in the problems of illusion and perspective. Where a cupola had originally been planned but had failed to be completed, he offered to paint a *trompe-l'-oeil* vault of staggering dimesions and effectiveness. The success of Pozzo's "fake" cupola was so great that he was asked to execute further major projects in the same church: first the immense ceiling of the nave (1685-1686) whose subject, "The Glory of St. Ignatius" is an anthology of Jesuit iconography. This gigantic work allowed the artist to display the lessons he had assimilated from all his great predecessors from Carracci to Gaulli as well as his genius at articulating figures. Pozzo was also entrusted with the design at altarpieces for the two chapels in the transept of the church. The drawing presented here is for the altar of St. Louis Gonzaga. By the time Pozzo took on this project, he had already been recognized for his design of the altar of St. Ignatius in the Gesù (1695-1697). In fact the artist clearly repeated in this design the one he had established previously, with only small variations. There are, however, considerable differences between the sketch exhibited here and the final altar which features in its center not a free standing saint resting on a pedestal, but the moving composition of Pierre Legros the Younger (a terracotta sketch for it is in the collections of the Detroit Institute of Arts). In 1700, a year after the completion of the altarpiece, Pozzo published his *Perspectiva Pictorum et Architectorum Andreae Putei e Societate Jesu,* a book which contained the reproductions of several designs related to this project.[J.P.M.]

Philadelphia Museum of Art, Bequest of Anthony M. Clark (1978-70-393)

18. *Study for the Altar of Saint Louis Gonzaga in Sant'Ignazio,* 1642-1709
Andrea Pozzo

GREGORIO DE FERRARI
1644—Genoa—1726

Born in Genoa, Gregorio de Ferrari went at an early age to Parma, where he studied and copied the ceiling paintings of Correggio. He then returned to Genoa, where he began to receive commissions for paintings. He was an extremely prolific artist, who painted many frescoes in Genoese churches. Correggio remained his most important inspiration throughout his career. Among Ferrari's frescoes, his most significant work is *The Assumption of the Virgin* in the church of SS. Giacomo and Philipp. His last major work is a *Triumph of the Cross* in the cupola of S. Croce in Rome, begun in 1720 and completed by his son, Lorenzo.

19. *The Glorification of the Name of Jesus*
    Pen and brown ink, brown wash, heightened with white, on blue-gray paper
    15 × 10 1/4 in. (38,8 × 26,3 cm)

Provenance: Purchased in London in 1962.

Literature: Gavazza, 1965, 38,39, verso fig. 39, as Lorenzo de Ferrari; Newcome, 1972, no. 143, the verso exhibited and represented as Lorenzo de Ferrari; Metropolitan Museum of Art exhibition, 1979.

The theme of the glorification of the name of Jesus was invented by the Jesuits, and was one of the most popular subjects during the seventeenth and eighteenth centuries for paintings in Jesuit churches. The most important example of this theme in seventeenth-century art is Gaulli's painting for the nave of the Gesù, in Rome. In Gaulli's work, painting, gold gilt, and stucco figures are combined to produce a masterful sense of optical illusion. The name of Jesus emanates from a blaze of near blinding light; stucco damned figures spill out into the church and painted blessed figures strive upwards feverishly as if pulled by a magnetic force to the source of light. In this design, Ferrari has reduced Gaulli's vast composition to four religious figures surrounded by flying putti. St. Ignatius Loyola sits on a cloud next to a model of a church gazing rapturously at the name of Jesus, while gesticulating towards the world below.[J.t.B.G.]

The Metropolitan Museum of Art, Rogers Fund (62.119.11)

20. *Design for a ceiling*
     Pen and wash on paper, squared for transfer
     16 × 10 in. (40,6 × 25,4 cm)

Inscription lower right: A. Pozzo

Provenance: Helene Seiferheld, New York.

Literature: Howard Hibbard, "The first painted decorations of the Gesù," *in Baroque Art, The Jesuit Contribution*, (New York: 1972); Bernhard Kerber, *Andrea Pozzo*, (Berlin and New York: 1971).

This drawing was apparently unknown to Bernhard Kerber, who did not include it in his monograph on the artist, but did not list it among the wrongly attributed drawings either. The attribution to Pozzo, which should be maintained with some caution, is confirmed by the inscription (although probably not autograph) as well as by iconographic and stylistic details.

The drawing appears to represent the preaching of one of the Apostles, perhaps Paul among the Athenians, a subject that was topical to the Jesuits, and which may have been, according to Howard Hibbard, one of the scenes selected for the decoration of one of the chapels in the original iconographic program for the Gesù.

One should also note the relationship between this drawing and the frescoes representing the *Glory of St. Francis Xavier*, executed in 1679 by Pozzo in the former Church of the Jesuits (Holy Martyrs and S. Francesco Saverio) in Mondori (see Kerber, *op. cit.*, 43-46, plate 28).[J.P.M.]

The Sheldon Swope Art Gallery, Terre Haute, Indiana [63.04]

FELIX ANTON SCHEFFLER
Munich 1701—Prague 1760

Active in the first half of the 18th century, Felix Anton Scheffler specialized in the production of frescoes, altarpieces, and devotional works for palaces and churches. He received his early training in Munich and Stuttgart. From 1730 until 1732, he worked in Schlesien; in 1732 he went to Prague. From the end of 1732 to 1747 he worked in Breslau as the court painter for the Bishop. In 1747 he returned to Prague, where he died. His commissions from the Jesuits in Breslau, Brünn, and Landsberg resulted in some of his most important paintings.

21. *St. Ignatius and the Four Parts of the World: Allegory of Jesuit Missionary Work*
    Pen and black ink, gray wash, heightened with white, over black chalk, on blue paper, squared in black chalk
    13 1/4 × 12 3/4 in. (33,8 × 32,5 cm)

The theme of St. Ignatius and the four parts of the world, invoked to serve as an allegory of Jesuit missionary work, is related to Andrea Pozzo's ceiling painting (1691-94) in Saint Ignazio, Rome. In a decorative roundal, which suggests the oculus of a cupola opening to the heavens, Sant' Ignazio, kneels beside a rock. Holding his *Spiritual Exercises,* he gazes rapturously upwards at the Holy Spirit, embodied in the Dove surrounded by flaming light and winged cherubs. Winged messangers fly out from the heavenly realm, holding candles with flames containing the name of Jesus. The four figures located outside the decorative molding symbolize the four parts of the world, each identified by appropriate attributes. The figure on the left, seated next to a domed church, stands for Europe; to her right a turbaned figure represents the Orient. The figure on the top-left, seated next to an elephant, represents Africa, and the figure to her right symbolizes the New World. The global nature of the Jesuit mission is suggested by the round shape of the central part of the design.

Stylistically, Scheffler's painting is related to Gaulli's fresco (1674-79) for the ceiling of the nave in the Gesù, Rome. Illusionistically painted architecture opening out to the heavens, with figures overstepping the painted illusion and moving into the viewer's space, is based on Gaulli's combining of painting with stucco figures in his design for the Gesù. His ceiling was, in turn, derived from Bernini's mixing of painting, sculpture and architecture (1645-52) in the Cornaro Chapel, in the church of Sta. Maria della Vittoria, in Rome.[J.t.B.G.]

The Metropolitan Museum of Art, Gift of the Estate of James Hazen Hyude (59.208.95)

21. *St. Ignatius and the Four Parts of the World: Allegory of Jesuit Missionary Work,* 1701-1760
Felix Anton Scheffler

CIRCLE OF GIUSEPPE ROLLI
17th Century

22.   *St. Ignatius in Ecstasy*
Pen, brown ink and wash with blue watercolor over graphite on laid paper.
20 1/4 × 12 1/8 in. (51,4 × 30,8 cm)

Provenance: Private collection, Rome; Dorothy Patterson Jackson, Dayton.

The activity of the Bolognese artist Giuseppe Rolli is recorded in various churches and palaces of his hometown, as well as in the Certosa of Pisa.

The attribution of this sheet, an advanced project for a ceiling fresco, is subject to further research. The intricate and richly decorated architecture betrays the influence of Angelo Michele Colonnam, a slightly earlier Bolognese artist who had specialized himself in the painting of perspectives and who is known to have played a part in the development of Rolli's style.

The architecture leads to a project for a cupola representing a frequent subject in Jesuit iconography: St. Ignatius praying in front of Christ's initials. Although the project was obviously intended for a Jesuit church, it is not known if it was executed.[J.P.M.]

The Dayton Art Institute, Gift of Mrs. Dorothy Patterson Jackson (76.37.3)

Prints

CHRISTOFFEL JEGHER
1596—Antwerp—1653

Christoffel Jegher was a draftsman and printmaker. In 1625 he began to work as an illustrator for the Officina Plantiana, the most important publishing house in Antwerp. Until 1643, Jegher produced woodcuts for major religious works published by Plantin; he was also one of the most accomplished masters who produced prints after the designs of Rubens.

23. *Temptation of Christ by the Devil*
    Woodcut, after Peter Paul Rubens
    12 3/4 × 17 in. (32,4 × 43 cm)

This woodcut reproduces a painting by Rubens in the north gallery of the Jesuit church in Antwerp. It depicts a key moment in the life of Christ, where He demonstrates His faith by resisting worldly temptations. A substantial part of the *Spiritual Exercises* is devoted to "Mysteries of the Life of Our Lord" from the annunciation to the ascension. Jegher's bold woodcut design simplifies Rubens' original composition into a memorable visual statement. The forceful illusionism of the ceiling painting translated into the print, gives the viewer the impression that the religious scene is actually physically taking place above him. The dense handling of line in Christ's drapery, that continues into the rock behind him, unifies Christ and the rock, asserting Christ's steadfastness in the face of temptation.[J.t.B.G.]

The Metropolitan Museum of Art, The Rogers Fund, 1917 (17.42.33)

24. *The Coronation of the Virgin*
    Woodcut, after Peter Paul Rubens
    12 3/4 × 17 in. (32,4 × 43 cm)

This woodcut reproduces Ruben's painting of this theme located at the west end of the south gallery in the Jesuit church, in Antwerp. Mary is seated on clouds in the middle of the painting. On her right is God the Father, his right hand clasping a sceptre and resting on a large orb, while his left hand stretches forth to support the crown as it is lowered on the Virgin's head. Christ stands to the left of the Virgin, and places the crown on the Virgin with both hands. Above the crown, the Holy Dove hovers in an aura of light.

The coronation of the Virgin by the Holy Trinity, in which Mary is Stationed between God the Father and the Son, appears in Flemish art as early as the fifteenth century. Rubens' treatment of the theme bears some resemblance to Vernonese's painting of the subject S. Sebastiano in Venice. The coronation of the Virgin was popular in Counter-Reformation iconography; it appears in the background of Bramer's *Glorification of Christianity*, in this exhibition. In Christian iconography, the coronation of the Virgin was a commonly understood metaphor for the Catholic church.[J.t.B.G.]

The Metropolitan Museum of Art, The Elijah Whittelsey Collection, V. Elijah Whittelsey Fund (67.79336)

JACOB DE WIT
Amsterdam 1695—Antwerp 1754

JAN PUNT
Antwerp 1711—Antwerp 1779

Set of engravings after Rubens ceiling paintings for the Jesuit church, Antwerp (destroyed by fire in 1718)

The Jesuit church in Antwerp, begun in 1615 and completed in 1621, is the most important example of the Jesuit contribution to the visual arts in northern Europe. The Flemish painter, Peter Paul Rubens, was commissioned to provide two altarpieces for the church, as well as a cycle of 39 ceiling paintings for the aisles and the galleries. Executed with the help of his assistant, Anthony van Dyck, the ceiling paintings are based on Rubens' close familiarity with Italian art of the Renaissance. A catastrophic fire destroyed the entire cycle in 1718; our knowledge of it today is based on the designs of copyists.

This set of engravings is based on drawings by the Dutch artist, Jacob de Wit. These drawings were translated into engravings by the Antwerp artist, Jan Punt. While the engravings included in the exhibition are not of exceptional aesthetic merit, they are of historical importance as documents of Rubens' lost picture cycle.[J.t.B.G.]

The Metropolitan Museum of Art, The Elijah Whittelsey Collection, The Elijah Whittelsey Fund.

25. *Title-Page*
     51.501.7249

26. *The Adoration of the Magi*
     51.501.7253

This scene was coupled with *Solomon and the Queen of Sheba*, which follows the conventional typology found in the *Biblia pauperum* and the *speculum humanae salvationis*. The text of the *Speculum* explains that the visit of Sheba, who came from the East bearing gifts for King Solomon, prefigures the offerings to the Christ Child by the three Kings.

27. *Melchizedek Offering the Bread and Wine to Abraham*
     51.501.7256

This scene from the Old Testament was seen as a prefiguration of *The Last Supper*, with which it is coupled in Rubens' picture cycle. Rubens has emphasized the mystical connection between the two subjects in several ways: the wine-jar and the basket seen on the steps in *The Last Supper* resemble those in the Old Testament scene, and there is an overt allusion to the meeting of Abraham and Melchizedek in the attitudes of Peter and the Lord, who are seated facing each other.

28. *The Prayer of Moses*
     51.501.7258

29. *Abraham's Sacrifice of Isaac*
51.501.7260

The Prayer of Moses finds its proper concordance in *Abraham's Sacrifice of Isaac,* which comes immediately after. The parallel is a venerable one, and may be found, for example, in the *Biblia pauperum.* The mystical meaning of Abraham's Sacrifice is expounded at length by biblical commentators, who observe that Isaac carried the wood to the mountain as Christ carried the cross to Mount Calvary, that Abraham signifies God the Father giving his only son, and that Isaac represents Jesus Christ, obedient to the Father, offering himself upon the altar of the cross. For this reason *The Sacrifice of Isaac* was also seen as a prefiguration of *The Crucifixion,* which is also included in Rubens' picture cycle.

30. *Esther before Ahasuerus*
51.501.7266

Learning from her cousin, Mordecai, that the king had decreed that all Jews should be put to death, the Jewish queen Esther went to Ahasuerus to intercede for her people. "As Esther spake yet again before the king, and fell down at his feet, and besought him with tears to put away the mischief of Haman . . . and his device that he had devised against the Jews. Then the king held out the golden sceptre toward Esther." (Esther VIII, 3-4). The exaltation of Esther is to be understood as prefiguring both *The Assumption* and *The Coronation of the Virgin;* this dual relationship is specifically affirmed by the Jesuit writer Vincenzo Bruno in his *Meditation on the Seven Principal Feasts of the Virgin [Meditationes in septem praecipua festa B. Virginis,* (Cologne: 1602) 234-5].

31. *St. Gregory of Nazianzus*
51.501.7274

St. Gregory of Nazianzus was one of the four Greek Church Fathers. As a great theologian who took a leading part in the struggle against Arianism, he may here be associated with the theme of orthodoxy triumphant over heresy. The smoke and flames that issue from the mouth of the vanquished demon are an attribute of Heresy.

32. *St. Lucy*
51.501.7278

Lucy was included in the cycle, along with St. Catherine, St. Barbara, and St. Eugenia, as one of the virgin martyrs. Depicted here suffering martyrdom, she exemplifies the steadfastness and self-sacrifice required of Jesuit missionaries who might find themselves facing death or torture.

33. *The Name of Jesus*
51.501.7281

The place of honor in each aisle was reserved for the Holy Names, that of Jesus on the left and that of Mary on the right. Rubens adheres to the recommendation of Molanus, who in his *Historia sacrarum imaginum et picturarum* (published in 1595/6) says that the name of Jesus should be painted amidst the rays of the sun [Migne, *Theologiae cursus completus,* XXVII, col. 183].

34. *St. Ambrose*
51.501.7283

It is told of this saint that, when as an infant he lay asleep in his crib, a swarm of bees descended upon his face and entered his mouth, after which they flew away so high that the eye could hardly follow them. The miracle was interpreted as foretelling the eloquence of the saint [Laurentius Surius, *Historiae, seu vitae sanctorum,* Turin, 1875-80, VI, p. 199]. Depicted with his attribute, the beehive, St. Ambrose was one of the four Latin Fathers of the Church.

MATTHEUS BORREKENS
1615—Antwerp—1670

35. *Portrait of St. Ignatius Loyola*
Engraving and etching, after Erasmus Quellinus
16 5/8 × 12 1/8 in. (42,3 × 30,9 cm)
Print Collection, Miriam and Ira D. Wallach, Division of Art, Prints, and Photographs,
The New York Public Library, Astor Lenox and Tilden Foundation

This portrait of St. Ignatius was made after the design of Erasmus Quellinus, a student of the Flemish painter, Peter Paul Rubens. The print is the title-page for the *Constitutiones Societatis Iesu*, published in Antwerp, by Martinus van Enden in the seventeenth century. The Latin text displayed by St. Ignatius comes from the "Preamble to the Constitutions:" "Although it must be the Supreme Wisdom and Goodness of God our Creator and Lord which will preserve, direct, and carry forward in His divine service this least Society of Jesus, just as He deigned to begin it, and although what helps most on our own part toward this end must be, more than any exterior constitution, the interior law of charity and love which the Holy Spirit writes and engraves upon our hearts; nevertheless, since the gentle arrangement of Divine Providence . . ."

Books and Maps

36. *Evangelicae historiae imagines*
Martin Nuntius, Antwerp, 1595/6

Literature: T. Buser, "Jerome Nadal and Early Jesuit Art in Rome," *Art Bulletin* 58 (1976) 424-433.

This volume, written by the Jesuit, Jerome Nadal, is one of the landmarks of sixteenth-century printing. The first part of it consists of a series of 153 engravings, mostly by the Wierix brothers, illustrating each of the Gospels read at the Mass on Sundays. Lettered captions beneath each engraving corresponding to letters of the alphabet are placed near the incidents depicted in the engravings. The second part of the book contains learned and exegetical annotations about each lettered incident, followed by a meditation or prayer.[J.t.B.G.]

The Lilly Library, Indiana University-Bloomington

37. *Imago primi saeculi Societatis Iesu*
    Plantin Press, Antwerp, 1640

This volume was produced by the Jesuits of Antwerp to celebrate their centenerary. Containing emblems, poems, and dissertations, the publication proclaims the victories of St. Ignatius Loyola and the Jesuit Order for the greater glory of God. The first emblem is that of the Society of Jesus (*Societas Iesu*) and shows a sun which shines on the world. The inscription, "*Non est qui se abscondat a calore eius* alludes to the idea that "the whole earth is illuminated by the propaganda of the Jesuits."[J.t.B.G.]

Marquette University, Memorial Library, Department of Special Collections and Archives

ANDREA POZZO
Trent 1642—Vienna 1700

38. *Prospettiva de Pittori ed Architetti*, 2 Vols., 1737
     Typography by Antonio de'Rubeis; published by Antonio de Possi, Rome 1737

Literature: Bernhard Kerber, *Andrea Pozzo* (Berlin and New York, 1971) 206,207

The first Italian and Latin edition of Pozzo's perspective book was published in Rome in 1693 (first part) and 1700 (second part). The publication encountered an immense success and was periodically reprinted throughout the 18th century.

The edition presented in the exhibition is the eleventh printing of the book in Rome (previous editions had included either the two parts of the book, or only one of the two).

In the case of this edition, the publication of the second part preceded that of the first part that took place in 1741 only. Pozzo's volumes were also published in other European languages during the 18th century. Editions in German, French, Flemish, English, Spanish, and modern Greek took place within a few years from the original Roman publication. It should also be noted that the Jesuit painter Giuseppe Castiglione helped with a translation in Chinese which had two printings. The Bibliothèque Nationale, Paris owns a copy of the original, published in Beijing in 1729.

In the exhibition, the book is opened at a page showing a model for an altar related to the one Pozzo designed for St. Ignatius at the Gesù in Rome.[J.P.M.]

Mead Art Museum, Amherst College, Museum Purchase (1984.14.1)

39.   Map of China from the *Atlante Veneto* [Venetian Atlas] by Coronelli (Venice, 1690]

Father Vincenzo Maria Coronelli (1650-1718), official Cosmographer of the Venetian Republic, was a man of religion, a learned geographer, a skilled mapmaker, and a successful entrepreneur. In 1671, Coronelli entered the Convent of S. Maria Gloriosa dei Frari in Venice, and by 1701 had risen to become General of the Order of Conventual Friars Minor. Though a Franciscan, it is the Jesuit contribution to Chinese cartography that Coronelli acknowledges on his map.

This map of China, originally engraved and published in two sheets, is dedicated to the "Most Reverend" Father Antonio Baldigliani of the Society of Jesus, Professor of Mathematics in the University of the College of Rome. In the northwest corner of the western map the cartouche features the monogram IHS, surrounded by a laurel wreath and radiating light. The titles of both sheets are set in an array of mathematical instruments with compass, dividers, globe, quadrant, and sundial.

A significant feature of Coronelli's approach to map-making is the appearance of descriptive notes on the map itself. Beneath the cartouche, is a statistical digest of Chinese geography. Divided into fifteen provinces, the map contains 1,312 principal citites, 2,357 secondary cities, and more. Some of the information was supplied by Father Filippo, Head of the Jesuit Mission in China, and like the map as a whole, it was derived from Chinese sources by Jesuit intermediaries.[J.B.H.]

American Georgraphic Society, University of Wisconsin-Milwaukee

40.   Ludovico Georgio, map of China in Ortelius's *Theatrum Orbis Terrarum* (Amsterdam, 1584)

Ludovico Georgio is identified by some authorities as a Portuguese Jesuit. However, in 1574 when he compiled the map of China in Ortelius's *Atlas,* he was working as a chartmaker and cosmographer for the Spanish crown.

In the sixteenth century much of the geographical information about China available to western European mapmakers came from Portuguese and Spanish trading voyages to Asia. The charts often remained in manuscript, or were deliberately kept secret. Among the sources for the map acknowledged in the Latin text on its verso are the Jesuit letters. The map represents a summation of European cartographic knowledge of China on the eve of the arrival of the Jesuits in Beijing at the beginning of the seventeenth century. It was the first separate map of China to be published in Europe, the first to show all fifteen Chinese provinces, and the first to locate so many cities and towns.[J.B.H.]

American Geographic Society, University of Wisconsin-Milwaukee

41.   Title page of the *Novus Atlas Sinesis a Martino* from J. Blaeu, *Atlas Maior sive Geographia Blaviana* (Amsterdam, 1662)

Martino Martinio was a Jesuit who was born in Trent in 1615 and died in Hangchow in 1661. After being educated in the Jesuit College in Rome, he was sent to China in 1643 where he travelled extensively. During his travels he collected books about the history and geography of China and fixed a number of latitudes and longitudes by taking astronomical observations. Among the materials that Martinio collected were detailed maps of China made by Chinese cartographers. He compiled these materials into an atlas of China designed for European readership.

The *Novus Atlas Sinesis,* published in 1655 in Dutch, French, German, and Latin, contained fifteen provincial maps, a map of Japan and Korea, and a general map of China. The engraving and typesetting of the accompanying geographical text were personally supervised by Martinio in Blaeu's workshop, who later incorporated the maps into his eleven-volume *Atlas Maior.*[J.B.H.]

American Geographic Society, University of Wisconsin-Milwaukee

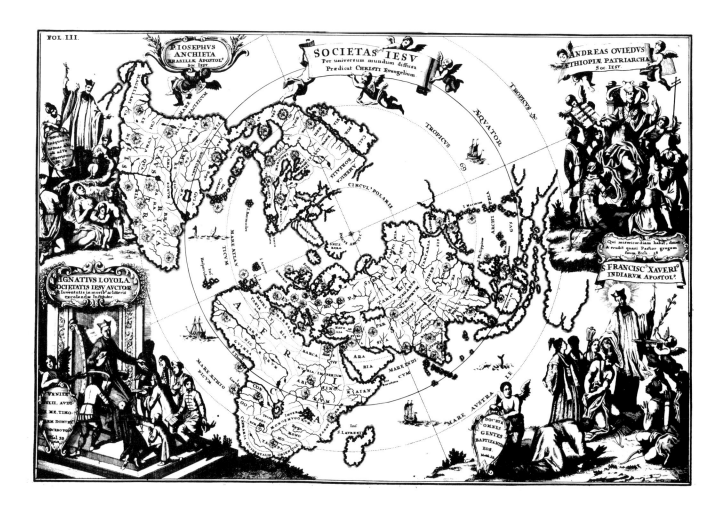

42.   Heinrich Scherer, World Map, from the *Atlas Marianus* (Munich, 1702)

Heinrich Scherer's map is a cartographic counterpart for Jesuit paintings, such as Pozzo's *Allegory of the Missionary Work of the Jesuits*, painted on the ceiling of S. Ignazio in Rome between 1691-94. Like Pozzo's fresco, the title cartouche of Scherer's map proclaims that the Society of Jesus would spread the faith throughout the world. Further confirmation of spiritual conquest is employed on the map. Each mission is located by a monogram for Christ's name ("IHS") and is surrounded by radiating light. In the corners of the engraving are allegorical portraits of four Jesuits—Andrew de Oviendo, Patriarch of Ethiopia; St. Francis Xavier, Apostle of India; St. Ignatius Loyola, founder of the order; and Father Joseph Anchieta, the Apostle of Brasil. Each is depicted preaching to groups of natives representing the four continents.

Heinrich Scherer (1628-1704) was a Jesuit and Professor of Geography and Mathematics at the University of Munich. This map was included in a manual of sacred geography, the *Atlas Marianus*, itself part of larger work the *Atlas Novus*, published between 1702 and 1703. Scherer compiled other maps which represent Jesuit world influence. These maps show the territorial boundaries of archbishoprics, bishoprics and missions, Jesuit educational establishments, and shrines of the Virgin Mary.[J.B.H.]

National Archives, Ottawa, Canada

Decorative Arts

43. INDIA, 18th CENTURY
     Chalice Pal
     Embroidered Silk
     24 × 24 in. (70 × 70 cm)

Chalice patens were used as covers for chalices filled with wine. This piece dates from the eighteenth century. It was produced either in China or in India before 1767, when the Jesuits were expelled from many of their missions. The name of Jesus and rays of light (the emblem of the Society of Jesus) are displayed here in delicate silk embroidery.[J.t.B.G.]

Courtesy of Valery Taylor Gallery, New York

44. JAPAN, 16th CENTURY
     Fume-i
     Wood with polychrome and guilding
     14 1/2 × 11 1/4 × 2 1/2 in. (36,8 × 28.6 × 6,4 cm)

This shallow wooden box contains an image of the Cross with the Virgin and Christ child in polychrome and gold leaf. Such boxes were made for secular purposes in Japan; however, the religious imagery here suggests a possible sacred function. The appearance of conventional Catholic imagery on a Japanese functional object may be associated with the Jesuit presence in Japan, as a part of their missionary effort.[J.t.B.G.]

The Snite Museum of Art, University of Notre Dame, Gift of Mr. and Mrs. James Alsdorf (87.35.40)

45. FLEMISH, 18th CENTURY
     Monstrance, *c.* 1725
     Silver
     23 inches tall
     St. Stanislaus Jesuit Historical Museum, Inc., 990.9

46. H. DeCurte
     Flemish, 18th CENTURY
     Chalice Pal
     Silver
     13 inches tall
     St. Stanislaus Jesuit Historical Museum, Inc., 990.10

47. FLEMISH, 18th CENTURY
     Set of Cruets
     Silver
     St. Stanislaus Jesuit Historical Museum, Inc., 990.11

Photographic Credits

Allen Memorial Art Museum, Oberlin College, cat. no. 17

Dirk Bakker, The Detroit Institute of Arts, cat. nos. 2, 8

Christie's New York, cat. no. 7

Clem Fiori, Princeton, New Jersey, cat. no. 6

Francis Ford, Milwaukee, cat. nos. 2, 37

Mead Art Museum, Amherst College, cat. no. 38

The Metropolitan Museum of Art, Photographic Services, cat. nos. 10, 12, 16, 18, 22

Museo de Arte de Ponce, cat. no. 3

The New York Public Library, cat. no. 35

Philadelphia Museum of Art, cat. nos. 5, 13, 14, 15, 19

Rollyn Puterbaugh, Dayton, Ohio, cat. no. 21

The Sheldon Swope Art Gallery, cat. no. 20

Valery Taylor Gallery, cat. no. 11

Bibliography

James S. Ackerman, "Della Porta's Gesù Altar," in *Essays in Honor of Walter Friedlaender* (New York: 1965) 1-2

James S. Ackerman, "The Gesù in the Light of Contemporary Church Design," *Baroque Art: The Jesuit Contribution*, ed. Rudolf Wittkower and Irma Jaffe (New York: Fordham University Press, 1972) 15-28.

J. C. H. Aveling, *The Jesuit* (New York: Steins and Day Publishers, 1982).

Paola Barocchi, *Trattati d'arte del Cinquecento, fra manierismo e controriforma* (Bari: Laterza, 1960-1962).

C. Beurdeley and M. Beurdeley, *Castiglione peintre jésuit à cour de Chine* (Fribourg: 1971).

J. Braun, *Die Belgischen Jesuitkirchen* (Freiburg: 1907).

Mario J. Buschizzo, "La Arquitectura en madera de las misiones del Paraquay, Chiquitos, Mojos y Maynas" in *Latin American Art, and the Baroque Period in Europe: Studies in Western Art III*, Millard Meiss et al. (Princeton: Princeton University Press, 1963) 173-190.

Thomas Buser, "Jerome Nadal and Early Jesuit Art in Rome," *Art Bulletin*, 58 (1976) 424-433.

N. Carbonieri, *Andrea Pozzo* (Trent: 1961).

Louis Chattelier, *The Europe of the Devout: The Catholic Reformation and the Formation of a New Society* (Cambridge: Cambridge University Press, 1989).

Carl G. Christensen, *Art and the Reformation in Germany* (Detroit/Athens, Ohio: Wayne State University Press/Ohio University Press, 1979).

Peter Daly, *Literature in the Light of the Emblem* (Toronto: Toronto University Press, 1979).

G. R. Dimler, "The Egg as Emblem: Genesis and Structure of a Jesuit Emblem Book," *Studies in Iconography* (1976) 85-106.

G. R. Dimler, "A Bibliographical Survey of Jesuit Emblem Books in German-Speaking Territories: Topography and Themes," *Arch. his. Soc. Iesu* (1976).

John P. Donnelly, S.J., "Antonio Possevino, S.J., as a Counter-Reformation Critic of the Arts," *Journal of Rocky Mountain Medieval and Renaissance Association* 3 (1982) 115-164.

J. Donohue, *Jesuit Education* (New York: 1963).

Carlos M. N. Eire, *War Against the Idols: The Reformation of Worship from Erasmus to Calvin* (Cambridge: Cambridge University Press, 1986).

Robert Enggass, *The Painting of Baciccio: Giovanni Battista Gaulli, 1639-1709* (Pennsylvania: University Park, 1964).

Evangelicae historiae imagines (Antwerp: 1594).

Joan Evans, *Monastic Iconography in France form the Renaissance to the Revolution,* (Cambridge: Cambridge University Press, 1970).

M. Fagiolo, "Struttura del Trionfo gesuitico: Baciccio e Pozzo," *Storia dell'Arte* (1980) 38-40, 353-360.

Ebria Feinblatt, "Early Jesuit Church Decoration," *The Art Quarterly* X, 4 (Autumn, 1947) 236-253.

David Freedberg, "The Representation of Martyrdoms during the Early Counter-Reformation in Antwerp," *Burlington Magazine* (1976) 128-138.

Sydney Freedberg, *Painting in Italy, 1500-1600 (Harmondsworth: Penguin Books, 1975).*

Charles Garside, Zwingli and the Arts (New Haven: Yale University Press, 1966).

I. Gerards-Neillsen, "Otto van Veen's *Emblemata Horatiana*," *Simiolus* 5 (1971) 20-63.

G. Gizchi and G. Matthiae, *S. Andrea al Quirinale* (Le Chiese di Roma illustrate, 107) (Rome: 1969).

Cornelis Goosens, "Nog meer over David Vinckboons," *Jaarboek van Het Koninklijk Museum Voor Schone Kunsten te Antwerpen* (1966) 59-106.

Joseph de Guibert, *The Jesuits: Their Spiritual Doctrine and Practice*, translated by William J. Young (Chicago: Loyola University Press, 1964).

Fernando G. Gutierrez, "A Survey of Modern Art" in *The Southern Barbarians: The First Europeans in Japan*, Michael Cooper, ed. (Tokyo and Palo Alto: Kodansha International in Cooperation with Sophia University, 1971) 147-206.

Francis Haskell, "The Role of Patrons: Baroque Style Changes," in *Baroque Art: The Jesuit Contribution*, ed. Rudolf Wittkower and Irma Jaffe (New York: Fordham University Press, 1972) 51-62.

Francis Haskell, *Patrons and Painters: A Study in the Relations between Italian Art and Society in the Age of Baroque*, 2nd ed. (New York: Alfred A. Knopf, 1963).

Julius Held, "Rubens and the *Vita Beati P. Ignatii Loiolae* of 1609," in *Rubens before 1620*, John R. Martin, ed. (Princeton: Princeton University Press, 1972) 93-132.

Arthur Henkel and Albrecht Schone, *Emblemata, Handbuch zur Sinnbildkunst des XVI. und XVII. Jahrhunderts* (Stuttgart: J.B. Metzler, 1967).

A. Herz, "Imitators of Christ: The Martyr-Cycles of Late Sixteenth Century Rome Seen in Context," *Storia dell'arte* 62 (1988) 53-70.

Howard Hibbard, "*Ut picturae sermones*: The First Painted Decorations of the Gesù," in *Baroque Art: The Jesuit Contribution*, ed. Rudolf Wittkower and Irma Jaffe (New York: Fordham University Press, 1972) 29-49.

William Hood, "Ciro Ferri's *Pensiero* for the Altarpiece of the Blessed Stanislaus Kostka in Sant'Andrea al Quirinale," *Bulletin. Allen Memorial Art Museum* 37 (1979-1980) 26-49.

Pierre Janelle, The *Catholic* Reformation (Milwaukee: Bruce, 1963).

Imago primi saeculi Societatis Iesu (Antwerp: 1640).

John B. Knipping, *Iconography of the Counter Reformation in the Netherlands* (Leiden: B. de Graff-Nieuwkoop/A. W. Sijthoff, 1974).

K. Künstle, *Ikonographie der Heiligen* (Freiburg im Breisgau: 1926).

Erik Larson and H. Minor, "Peter Paul Rubens and the Society of Jesus," *Konshistorisk Tidskrift* (1977) 48-54.

Irving Lavin, "Bernini's Death," *Art Bulletin* 54 (1972) 158-186.

T.M. Lucas, S.J. ed., *Saint, Site and Sacred Strategy: Ignatius, Rome, and Jesuit Urbanism*, (Rome: Biblioteca Apostolica Vaticana, 1990).

Romeo de Maio, *Michelangelo e la controrinforma* (Bari: Laterza, 1978).

Emile Mâle, *Religious Art in France: The Thirteenth Century*, (Princeton: Princeton University Press, 1984).

Emile Mâle, *L'art religieux après le Concile de Trente* (Paris: A. Colin, 1932).

John R. Martin, *The Ceiling Paintings for the Jesuit Church in Antwerp, Corpus Rubenianum Ludwig Burchard* I (Brussels: Arcade Press, 1968).

J. D. C. Masheck, "The Original High Altar Tabernacle of the Gesù rediscovered," *Burlington Magazine* 112 (1970) 110-113.

M. Mauquoy-Hendrickx, "Les Wierix illustrateurs de la Bible dite de Natalis," *Quarendo* 6 (1976) 28-63.

C. J. McNapsy, "Art in Jesuit Life," in *Studies in the Spirituality of Jesuits*, v. 3 (1973).

C. J. McNapsy, *Lost Cities of Paraquay: Art and Architecture of the Jesuit Reductions, 1607-1767* (Chicago: Loyola University Press, 1982).

See C. F. Menestrier, *La philosophie des images énigmatiques* (Lyons: 1694).

L. H. Monssen, "*Rex Gloriose Martyrum:* A Contribution to Jesuit Iconography," *Art Bulletin* (1981) 130-137.

Jennifer Montagu, "The Painted Enigma and French Seventeenth-Century Art," *Journal of the Warburg and Courtauld Institutes* 31 (1968) 307-335.

L. Montalato, "Andrea Pozzo nella Chiesa di Sant'Iganzio al Collegio Romano," *Studi romani* 6 (1958) 668-679.

Jerome Nadal, *Imagines de la Historia Evangelica* (Antwerp: 1593/94), ed. by A. de Ceballos (Barcelona: 1975).

Erik Neumann, "Das Figurenrelief auf der Urne des Hl. Ignazio im römischen 'Gesù'," *Pantheon* 35 (1977) 318-328.

Antonio T. de Nicholas, *Powers of Imagining: Ignatius de Loyola* (New York: State University of New York Press, 1986).

Jaroslav Pelikan, *Imago Dei: The Byzantine Apology for Icons* (Princeton: Princeton University Press, 1990).

W. A. M. Peters, *The Spiritual Exercises of St. Ignatius* (Jersey City: Program to Adapt the Spiritual Exercises, 1968).

Ander Pigler, *Barockthemen*, 3 volumes (Budapest: 1974).

Pietor Pirri, *Giovanni Tristano e i primordi della architettura Gesuitica* (Rome: 1955).

Pietro Pirri, *Giuseppe Valeriano, S.I.: architetto e pittore, 1542-1596* (Rome: 1970). Mario Praz, *Studies in Seventeenth-Century Imagery*, 2 volumes (Rome: Edizioni di Storia e Letteratura, 1964).

Paolo Prodi, "Ricerche sulla teorica delle arte figurative nella riforma cattolica" in *Archivo italiano per la storia della pietà* 4 (1965) 121-212.

L. Puhl, trans., *Spiritual Exercises of St. Ignatius* (Chicago: Loyola University Press, c. 1951).

D. Redig de Campos, "Intorno a due quadri d'altare del Van Dyck per il Gesù di Roma ritrovati in Vaticano," *Bolletino d'arte* 30 (1936-1937) 150-165.

Louis Richeôme, *La peinture spirituelle* (Lyon: 1611).

E. Schaar, "Carlo Marattas *Tod les heiligen Franz Xavier* in Gesù," in *Munuscula Discipulorum. Kunsthistorische Studien Hans Kauffmann zum 70. Geburtstag 1966*, ed. T. Budensieg and M. Winner (Berlin: 1968) 247-264.

H. Schadt, "Andrea Pozzos Langhausfresko in S. Ignazio, Rome. Zur Themen-tradition der barocken Heiligenglories," *Das Munster* 24 (1971) 153-160.

H. J. Schroeder, *Canons and Decrees of the Council of Trent* (St. Louis: Herder, 1941).

G. Schurhammer, *Francis Xavier, his life, his times. Europe 1506-1541* (Rome: 1973).

Jonathan D. Spence, *The Memory Palace of Matteo Ricci* (New York: Random House, 1984).

J. N. Tylenda, S.J., *Jesuit Saints & Martyrs* (Chicago: Loyola University Press, 1984).

J. Vanuxem, "Les Jésuits et la peinture au XVIIe siècle à Paris," *La Revue des Arts* 8 (1958) 85-91.

Horst Vey, "A Vision of St. Ignatius of Loyola during the Writing of the Rules of the Jesuits," *Master Drawings* II (1964) 268-271.

Hans Vlieghe, "Rubens's Activity for the Ghent Jesuits in 1633," *Burlington Magazine* 111 (1969) 427-435.

M. B. Wadell, "The *Evangelicae Historiae Imagines:* The designs and their artists," *Quarendo* 10 (1980) 279-291

P. Wilberg-Vignau, *Andrea Pozzos Deckenfresko in S. Ignazio. Mit einem Anhang: Archivalische Quellen zu den Werken Pozzos* (Munich: 1970).

Rudolf Wittkower, "Problems of the Theme," in *Baroque Art: The Jesuit Contribution*, ed. Rudolf Wittkower and Irma Jaffe (New York: Forhamd University Press, 1972) 1-14.

Rudolf Wittkower, *Art and Architecture in Italy, 1600-1750* (London: Penguin Books, 1965).

Frances Yates, *The Art of Memory* (Chicago: University of Chicago Press, 1966)

F. Zeri, *Pittura e Controriforma* (Turin: 1957).